SOME
RAIN
MUST
FALL

Cover by James Converse

SOME RAIN MUST FALL

by Elizabeth Spalding
McFadden

Thy fate is the common fate of all,
Into each life some rain must fall.—Longfellow

Pacific Press Publishing Association
Mountain View, California   Omaha, Nebraska

CONTENTS

Chapter		Page
1	Into the Valley	1
2	The Shadows Lift	8
3	Mountain Town	14
4	Not India, but Chicago	22
5	Where He Leads	29
6	Rainbow Trails	34
7	High Noon	44
8	India at Last!	53
9	Birth of a New Nation	59
10	Out to the Villages	65
11	The Shadow Descends	72
12	Night	82
13	The Break of Dawn	87

1 - INTO THE VALLEY

If Wayne had been watching, he would have come bounding down the steps to welcome Karen with open arms. But he was not watching, and Karen strode by on the opposite side of the street, careful not to betray her feelings by more than a casual glance toward his house.

Leapin' Lizzie stood in the driveway, evidence that Wayne was at home. But he was not delving into the innards of the old Model A as he usually did on Friday afternoon. Karen had so hoped he would be there today—oh, please, at least today! But he was not there, and all her resolutions began to crumble.

For a moment she wavered. It would be so simple to dash across the street, press the doorbell, and say the two short words, "I'm sorry." But Karen could not make herself do it, much as she wanted to. And now she had passed his house.

Wistfully she thought about Leapin' Lizzie, as she and Wayne had dubbed the old car when he had bought it two years before. She remembered helping him brush on the coat of dark-green paint. Later they had waxed the car together.

"If we keep enough wax on these fenders, it will delay rusting by two or three years," he had explained. "We can't afford to paint her again till after we're through medical school, honey, so we'd better take good care of this job."

He stopped to flash a quick smile at Karen. Nodding in agreement, she picked up the rag and energetically polished some more. How Lizzie glistened when they stepped back to admire her! And how Wayne's eyes shone as he stole frequent glances at his fiancée, her face smudged with dirt, her brown hair curling around her sweaty forehead.

But that was long ago when they had first come to medical school. Now they were nearing the end of their junior year at the College of Medical Evangelists, and the old car was beginning to show signs of neglect and wear. It had weathered many a purposeful detour through orange groves on moonlit nights and hard pulls up curving mountain roads to the snow-capped peaks. Gay and carefree days those had been. They had spent golden hours together discussing plans for the future. They would be missionaries—go to India, perhaps, and set up a mission hospital where they could labor together.

Karen sighed. Since the little car, like their other interests, had ceased to be a joint project, it received no attention from Karen and very little from Wayne. He kept it running just well enough to make monthly trips home where his aging mother waited for his visits.

Karen remembered her last trip home with Wayne. On the day before Thanksgiving he had caught her by surprise after class with the unexpected question, "How would you like to go home with me for Thanksgiving dinner, Karen?"

Because they had hardly spoken to each other since their quarrel two months before, Karen nearly lost her balance and tripped over the doormat in front of the chemistry building. Reaching out a hand to steady her, Wayne caught her eyes with his, searching deeply. Trying to be casual, she smiled lightly at him and answered, "That would be fun, Wayne. I've hardly been off this campus for three months!"

The trip was a failure. Although Mrs. Wells welcomed Karen warmly, it was difficult for the girl to play a double role. In his mother's presence Karen must pretend that everything between Wayne and herself was as it had been, while deep in her heart she knew it could never be the same again, unless—

When they were alone in Leapin' Lizzie, Wayne's pleading eyes told more than he would allow his lips to utter. He stumblingly apologized for his part in the quarrel, but she did not forgive him, and he did not mention the subject again. Karen knew the next move was up to her. The trouble had been mostly her fault, yet she could not bring herself to make up with him.

She felt as if this were all a bad dream, as if Wayne were not really sitting over there on his side of the car, making no attempt to draw her closer. Soon she would wake up and everything would be all right. They would be talking of their plans after medical school, of where they would intern, of their wedding, of a call to the mission field. But the horrible dream lasted the whole day long. When she forced herself to smile and kiss his mother good-bye, she felt that this could possibly be her last visit to his home. On the way back to Los Angeles she and Wayne talked of a number of trivial things.

Safely in bed that night, Karen cried herself to sleep. She did love Wayne, and she knew he loved her. Then why couldn't she say the words that would set things right? Wayne had given her the opening, but she had been too proud! She buried her face in her pillow and dreamed of Wayne reaching out his arms to her, of wedding bells ringing.

Now it was February. Karen thought and planned what she would say to Wayne to patch things up, but the opportunity never seemed to come. Finally she told herself that this nonsense must stop! She would just walk over to his house and tell him.

"Wayne," she would say, "I am the one who was wrong. I'm the one who needs to apologize. I'm sorry, and I love you."

"It would be simple," she told herself as she set out for his rooming house that Friday afternoon. Maybe he would be working on his car; then she wouldn't have to risk meeting some other medic coming to the door when she rang the bell. But he was not outside. Panic struck her, and pretending not even to notice the place, she strode on toward the County Hospital. "If he sees me," she thought, "he will only think I'm on my way to complete some assignment at the County."

3

"Go back, Karen! Go back and knock on his door!" her heart kept telling her. But her feet marched relentlessly, like the steady beat of drums in the night, leading her away from the man she loved.

After spending an hour wandering aimlessly through the wards of the huge county hospital, now and then stopping to check an interesting case, Karen started back along the street to her dormitory. She would pass Wayne's rooming house again, and maybe this time he would be out working on the car. But again she was disappointed. So near and yet so far. Just twenty steps up his driveway. Just one push on the doorbell—

Quickening her pace, Karen choked back tears of frustration and glanced at her watch. It was nearly five o'clock! There was still her dress to press for Sabbath, her hair to fix.

"Maybe I'll see him at MV tonight," she thought, "or maybe at supper. I'll tell him then, I really will."

But Wayne did not come to the cafeteria that night, at least not while Karen lingered there, making her food last as long as she dared. Nor was he in Missionary Volunteer meeting. She went to bed with a heavy heart, determined to end the useless suspense the very next time she saw him, even if that was during church.

Sabbath morning Karen dressed carefully. This was to be The Day to End the Quarrel, and she wanted to look her best. She took a seat near the back of the church where she could watch everyone come in. His class was near the front. She had often been glad hers was behind it because she could steal a sly glance in his direction without his knowing it.

Suddenly someone tapped her on the shoulder.

"Pardon me, Karen, but could you tell me how to get in touch with Wayne Wells's mother?" It was Tom Smith speaking.

"Why? Is something wrong with Wayne?"

"Yes, I'm afraid so."

Instantly Karen was on her feet following Tom into the vestibule. "What's wrong, Tom? You must tell me!"

Tom hesitated, then apparently decided she had a right to know.

"I took him to the hospital this morning. He is a very sick boy. They aren't sure what's wrong, but they've put him in the contagious ward over at the County. It—well—it looks like it might be meningitis!"

"Oh, no!" cried Karen. "Not Wayne! He's always been so healthy!" She fumbled in her purse for a handkerchief, choking back the tears. "Will they let me see him, Tom?"

"I don't know," Tom said quietly. "We can try."

Riding beside Tom in Leapin' Lizzie, Karen sat tense and erect. Tom told her that he had heard Wayne moaning in his room early that morning. He went in to see what was wrong and found Wayne tossing on the bed and complaining of a splitting headache. His temperature was high. Tom called the men's dean, who secured the services of a doctor within an hour. The doctor recommended that they get Wayne into the county hospital at once.

"They're more fully equipped than our hospital to give the tests I want right now," he explained. At the County, tests were begun at once. Wayne's condition had grown steadily worse.

"When I left," Tom finished, "he seemed to be almost in a coma!"

Karen jumped from the car before Tom had brought it to a complete stop. She dashed ahead to the contagious disease ward, learned that Wayne was in a private room, and donned the necessary cap, gown, and mask to be allowed to enter.

Wayne did not know her! Throwing caution to the wind, she knelt by his bed, begging him to forgive her. Oblivious of Tom and of the nurse working over Wayne, she poured into his unhearing ears the words she knew he had been longing to hear. Wayne only moaned in his delirium and turned unseeing eyes upon her. Karen could not restrain the tears and withdrew to the window to give the nurses and doctors more room to work. She pleaded with God for Wayne's recovery. She realized that if she had only stopped to see him yesterday she might have gotten help for him earlier!

Through the hours that followed, Karen did not leave the bedside for more than a few minutes at a time. Wayne's mother arrived with one of his older brothers. She treated them kindly, telling them all she could about Wayne's sickness, but not mentioning her own private torture—the fear that he might never regain consciousness or be able to forgive her!

The doctors consulted with each other and reached a diagnosis of spinal meningitis. There was little that could be done* except to relieve the symptoms. An icepack was applied to the patient's neck; he was fed intravenously and given constant nursing care. The doctor tried to break the news gently to Wayne's aging mother that there was little hope for his recovery. Helplessly Karen watched the light of hope go out in the mother's care-lined face. Wayne was all she had left. Her other boys were married, and none of them shared with her the advent faith as Wayne did. She had sacrificed all she had to give Wayne a medical education.

As the hours ticked slowly by, Karen watched as the dreadful disease sapped Wayne's strength. The next day came, and still there was no turn for the better. By the second night Wayne was too weak to move a finger. Still she hovered near, hoping and praying that he would regain consciousness.

Before dawn Tuesday morning Wayne Wells was gone. Karen stumbled from the room, too grief-stricken to comfort his poor mother but for a moment.

"Too late!" she sobbed into her pillow as dawn broke over the college campus. "Too late! Oh, why did I put it off so long?"

Picking up the threads of life was not easy for young Karen Anderson. Through long nights she questioned God's wisdom in allowing Wayne to die. Hadn't they planned to serve Him together in India? Here was a young doctor halfway through his training, a good Christian boy—the very best! Why did God allow him to be taken?

Gradually her thoughts aligned themselves in order, and she could feel God encircling her with His love. Surely God in His wisdom knew best. Perhaps Wayne would have met insurmountable temptations in years to come. She searched her own life,

---

*Antibiotics had not yet been discovered.

6

wondering if she would be ready if a sudden call came to her. Finally, through prayer, she found her footing again.

Plunging into her studies with a determination to do the work of two doctors if need be, she finished her senior year with honors and took the well-deserved diploma with satisfaction. Staring through her tears at Wayne's vacant chair with the ribbon draped across it, she kept locked in her heart the secret that she had been too late, and Wayne had died never knowing of her love!

A new determination took hold of her on graduation night. She would make good. Wayne would be proud to meet her when they were reunited in heaven. He would know then that because of her love for him she had accomplished all she could for God. For him she had answered the call to the mission field, alone.

2- THE SHADOWS LIFT

When Karen arrived in Boulder, Colorado, for her internship, the depression was at its worst and the sanitarium had few patients. Although only a minimal fee was charged, few seemed able to afford even that. Many who became ill remained at home, being nursed by loving mothers, sisters, or aunts. One or two lonesome babies occupied the ten-bassinet nursery, and the four-bed wards were lucky to house two patients at a time.

Dr. Klopfenstein, the medical director, was naturally a hustler. Bored with the small amount of work he was able to obtain at the sanitarium, he set out to find something more to do. The county hospital five miles away was full to overflowing; so he arranged to do some free work there and invited young Dr. Anderson to accompany him.

"You know," he told her enthusiastically, "you could help me, too, if you want to. You need more experience than these few patients here at the San can give you."

To this Karen gladly agreed. She would far rather be busy than sit mulling over the past. She remembered, too, what Wayne had once said, "County hospitals will offer us more of the type of patients we will find in the mission field. That's where we should intern if we possibly can."

Well, now she was to have experience in a county hospital, and Karen had a feeling that it would be good training.

Since Dr. Klopfenstein lived across the road from the county hospital, he was often called for emergencies. One evening he re-

8

ceived a call to go to the home of an old man. "We've tried to get these folks to bring the patient to the hospital, but they say he is too old. Nearly a hundred," the county nurses told the doctor.

Since it was still early, Dr. Klopfenstein decided to invite Karen to go with him. Karen was happy for something to do, and they rode along together in the doctor's car trying to follow the sketchy directions the people at the hospital had given them. At last they found the tumbledown shack belonging to an old man whom they later dubbed "the centenarian."

Entering the low-ceilinged, evil-smelling dwelling, they found the man lying on an old iron bed, covered with a ragged quilt. His breathing was labored, his fever high. The two doctors agreed upon a diagnosis of pneumonia.

"You'll have to go to the hospital," Dr. Klopfenstein informed the old man. Turning to the man's friend, an oldster not much younger than the patient, the doctor began to give instructions about getting him to the hospital. Suddenly there was a stir in the bed.

"Wait a minute, doc," called the sick man, bracing himself on his elbow. "I ain't goin' to no hospital. Ef I'm a gonna die, here's good a place 's anywhere!"

He fell back into the dirty bedclothes and yielded to a fit of coughing. But he seemed determined, and his companion shook his head.

"If'n he's made up his mind, doc, there ain't much nobody kin do 'bout it," he said. "I'll do what I kin fer him here."

Seeing that it was useless to argue further, Dr. Klopfenstein left medicine and instructions and departed. But in the car he shook his head. "It's doubtful whether he will live through the night," he told Karen. "But if he does, maybe we can persuade him to go to the hospital tomorrow. He needs an oxygen tent."

The next morning the two doctors were called again and urged to "come immediately" to the old man's house. They were surprised to find the sheriff's car in the yard and several men in the house, including the county coroner. On the floor covered with a sheet lay the old man who had been the "nurse" the night before. In the bed the old centenarian, fire still flashing from his eyes, was stubbornly refusing to answer the sheriff's questions.

The "nurse," they learned, had been trying to persuade his charge to go to the hospital. Suddenly the old man had reached under his pillow and pulled out his gun. His closest neighbors, hearing a shot, came running, only to find the "nurse" lying on the floor in a pool of blood. He had breathed his last as the sheriff drove into the yard.

Now, the officers wondered, what would they do with the old man? He was too sick to arrest. The next best thing, they decided, was to send him to the county hospital, but some sedation must be given to get him there. This, too, presented a problem. The gun still lay beside his pillow, and only the centenarian himself knew whether or not it was still loaded. Outside on the porch the men planned a strategic move, but decided to leave Dr. Anderson out of it. This was too dangerous a job for a woman!

Karen was a bit indignant. Here was something exciting. Why couldn't she be in on it, too?

"If Wayne were only here—" her thoughts began, but she cut them off abruptly.

Inside, everything was quiet, like the stillness before a whirlwind. Karen waited impatiently. "He is like a child," she thought—like Lewis, her little redheaded brother, who used to lose his temper. When that happened she had left him alone for a while. Later he would come hunting for her, sheepishly admitting that playing by himself was no fun.

Suddenly from inside the cabin came angry shouting.

"You fellows get out and leave me alone!" rasped the old man. Then he lapsed into another coughing spell.

Several rather white-faced men backed out of the door onto the front porch. "He turned the gun on us!" they chorused.

Karen, determined to treat the old man like a child, brushed past the sheriff. Calmly she approached the bed, talking gently to the old man. His gun, she noticed, had fallen to the pillow.

"Grandpa," she said kindly, "we came to help you, but if you don't want our help we will just go away and leave you alone. But," she added, "you really need help, you know."

She backed carefully toward the door, watching him.

Slowly his eyes lost their fire. His hands shook, and he was only a poor, sick old man again.

"Yep, I need help—but not from them fellows," he whispered. "You helped me last night; you do it now!"

Karen reached for her bag, quickly prepared a sedative injection, and administered it to the unresisting patient. Fifteen minutes later the slumbering patient was hospital-bound in the sheriff's car.

The officers wondered what charge to make. They carefully studied the cabin and its contents. They examined the old man's gun. It was badly rusted, and the officers could not make it fire although they tried repeatedly. They finally decided to list the shooting as accidental and make no charge against the sick old man.

From that day on Dr. Anderson was the only one the centenarian wanted. Often she spent time at his bedside, cheering him and helping to banish his loneliness with her presence.

"Grandpa," she said to him one day, "you have lived a long time in this old world. Why!" the sudden thought occurred to her, and she spoke it aloud before she thought, "you must have been born before the stars fell!"

"Born in 1833," he answered. "My mother used t' say, 'Spring is th' best time to born a youngster.' Reckon that was 'cause I was so strong and healthy. Stars fell, ye say? Mmmmm. Seems t' me my mother did used t' talk 'bout that."

"What did she say?" asked Karen, unable to restrain her eagerness.

"Mmmm—her and Aunt Katie used t' mention that the year I was borned the heavens well nigh fell in on all of us! Seems father saw it first—when he went out to milk, I reckon. Used ter go early-like, I 'member—4 a.m., mebbe. That night th' stars fell, he waked my mother up to see it—it was that much, I guess, and he was kind of scared. Thought mebbe th' end of th' world was coming."

11

"Really? Did your aunt see it, too?"

"Yep, she sure did. She and mother told me 'bout it from the time I was a little shaver. Some of my older cousins 'membered it, too. Must've been quite a show!"

"It must have been," Karen agreed, thrilled to hear almost a first-person account of it. Then she told him how the falling of the stars was one of the signs mentioned in the Bible to precede the second coming of Christ. The old man listened attentively, nodding his head all the time. Yes, he knew about that. His mother had said it was in the Bible.

"And, grandpa," Karen concluded, "I want to be ready when Jesus comes, don't you?"

"Yep. Sure do," agreed the old man. "I try to be helpful 'round here. Make my bed and help th' nurses all I kin. I reckon as how God won't pass me by in th' end."

"Yes, you are helpful, grandpa." Karen smiled at him. "But you have to have your sins forgiven, too. Would you like me to have prayer with you before I go?" The old man slipped his stocking cap off and closed his eyes while the doctor prayed. When it was over, he said huskily, "Thank 'e, doctor."

Karen smiled and patted his hand before she left.

About six months after he had entered the hospital, he reached his hundredth birthday, and it was Karen who planned the large cake with 100 candles on it. The whole hospital staff turned out to celebrate! The old man sang the praises of "my lady doctor" until he died at the age of 102.

At the county hospital Karen met Juanita Clark, a nurse with whom she became fast friends. Early one morning, as Karen stumbled from the delivery room after a particularly difficult time, she was close to tears. Miss Clark, who had been in and out of the delivery room helping in any way she could, realized that Dr. Anderson was near the breaking point and followed her into the dressing room.

"It wasn't your fault, Dr. Anderson," she said. "It was just one

12

of those things. You saved the mother; that in itself was a miracle."

Karen's eyes brimmed. "Oh, that poor little mother! She *wanted* that baby so badly!"

"I know," whispered the nurse, "but you did your best. Listen!" she continued, as an impulse struck her. "Why don't you come home and have breakfast with me? We'll fix some waffles, and mother just bought some maple syrup yesterday."

Karen accepted, mostly to please Juanita. She soon found Juanita's cheerfulness contagious. The nurse's mother, too, made her feel at home. In the days which followed, Karen often relaxed in their spacious living room or enjoyed the view from the veranda of their hilltop home. She spent happy hours listening to Juanita's records and just talking with the family. Mr. Clark was seldom home, but Mrs. Clark and Juanita and Kathy, the younger sister, made Karen feel like a part of the family. Eventually they discussed religion, and Karen found a number of opportunities to share her beliefs. Juanita became her almost constant companion, and it seemed natural for her to accept Karen's invitation to attend church with her.

Karen persuaded Juanita and her mother to study the Bible with her, and they began the following week. Kathy sat in on a few of the studies but soon lost interest. Both Juanita and Mrs. Clark were interested students and seemed convinced of the truths Karen presented. When they came to the study on the Sabbath, Juanita said, "I'm sure the Bible is right on this, and your church is the only one I know of which follows this commandment. Oh, Karen, I want to join your church and keep the Sabbath!"

Karen was thrilled. She thanked God for giving her such a wonderful experience. A few months later she sat near the front of the church as Juanita was baptized. Mrs. Clark could not bring herself to make so drastic a change in her life, but she did not discourage Juanita from taking the step.

"Just think," mused Karen contentedly, "I can be a missionary right here at home." The thought was comforting, for who could tell whether or not she would ever receive a call to a foreign field?

3- MOUNTAIN TOWN

"Which way to Nederland?" Karen inquired.

The old miner scratched his head. "Well," he drawled, "it's that way, about ten miles, young lady." He pointed to his left.

It was Sunday and nearing sundown. Karen had intended to arrive before dark, but a right-hand fork had fooled her, and she had driven several miles out of the way before she realized it.

"Don't know's I've seen you around here before. You got friends up in Nederland?" the miner asked.

"No," Karen answered, hoping not to prolong the conversation.

"You could spend the night here, ma'am," he offered politely. "Might be kinda hard to find a new town after dark. My missus 'n me, we'd be proud to put ya up fer a night."

"Thanks so much," answered Karen, warming to his hospitality. "I'm Dr. Karen Anderson, and this is my mother, Mrs. Anderson." She indicated the passenger beside her. "Thanks again, but we did want to get to Nederland tonight."

"Well, I'll be! A lady doctor, huh?" the man rubbed his brow and stared at her.

"You think it's the left fork?" Karen prodded him.

"Yep. Well, if ye be so set on goin', just follow that fork to the end of the road and turn left—there's signs along the way. Ya can't miss it."

Karen nodded, thanked the man, and headed the struggling Ford coupe up the grade. No wonder the car had trouble climbing these mountain roads; it was loaded with medical supplies, paint,

14

wallpaper, clothes, a hundred-pound sack of potatoes, a large tin of dried beans—

"We can't starve as long as we have potatoes and beans, Karen," mother had remarked when they were packing.

Karen glanced appreciatively at her mother's profile in the gathering darkness. Dear mother! She was sweet to embark on this wild new venture with her restless daughter. Mother had spent many years as a nurse. Every time a neighbor's child was sick or a new baby was born, mother had gone. Karen could never remember her mother's turning down a call to help. In the years after Karen's father had died, nursing had been the family's bread and butter. But mother was in her late sixties now, and Karen hoped this adventure would not prove to be too much for her.

When Karen first heard of the need for a doctor in the mountain town of Nederland, Colorado, she was nicely settled in Boulder. She was not getting rich, but she was busy. Still, there were plenty of doctors in Boulder, and, besides, she had always loved pioneering. A needy town like Nederland, she reasoned, would be almost like the mission field. She would feel needed!

The cabin she planned to occupy had been offered free of rent as as inducement to move to Nederland. Karen tried to find a nurse, but none would consider such an out-of-the-way place. Finally Mrs. Anderson, who had been keeping house for her daughter in Boulder, suggested, "Why don't you let me help you, Karen? With only two rooms to keep up, I'm sure I can assist you when you need me in the office."

"But mother, you aren't so young anymore. I'm afraid it would be too much for you."

"Nonsense! I'm still able to hobble around a bit, I guess!"

Karen was afraid she had hurt her mother's feelings, so she laughed and said, "Well, you know I'd love having you work with me."

Now Karen peered into the darkness before her, watching carefully the twists and turns of the mountain road. Tiny flakes of snow began to appear on the windshield.

"Oh, mother! How will we ever find the place in a snowstorm?"
"There's no snowstorm yet, Karen," answered her mother, "only a few flakes floating down. Besides, we must be almost there."

Sure enough, around the next curve was the town. Now to find the cabin. Karen recited the directions she had been given:

"In town, on the main street, you'll come to a grocery store on the right. Just beyond, you'll see a sign with an arrow pointing right. It will say, 'Carlson's Cove,' and you take that lane up the hill. Half a block from the main road you'll see the cabin on the left. It is—or was—white, with green trim. It's right on the street; your shingle will be easy to see when you hang it out."

There was the grocery store. Now a little farther and turn right. Karen skidded the wheels a bit on the pine needles as she brought the car to a stop in front of the cabin.

Karen and her mother pulled their suitcases from the shambles of the car trunk and made up their rickety old cots. That night the snow fell thick, but Monday was a pleasant day. They unpacked and stored their clothes and supplies in their little shelter, with the wood stove sending off welcome drafts of heat. Luckily, the owner had left some chopped wood beside the stove when he closed the cabin for the season. It was nice to feel cozy and safe while outside the wind blew the snow about like plum-blossom petals.

Monday night they pulled the first strip of old paper from the walls of the "office." They continued working for the next three days until the cabin was quite presentable. The walls were decorated with a twined-ivy-patterned paper, and the wood paneling was painted white.

"Is this where the new doctor lives?" A woman's voice brought Karen from the depths of her improvised closet. It was Wednesday noon.

"Yes," the doctor called. "Just sit down, won't you? I'll be out in a moment." A glance in the tiny mirror, a quick brush of her hair, and she presented herself to her first patient.

"She's had a mighty bad fever since Sat'day night," the woman explained, "but we couldn't get out of our house, 'twas snowing so! Soon's I could, I told my husband, I was gonna get her to the new doctor. So here she is!"

Carefully Karen examined her patient, a little girl who stared at her apprehensively from large blue eyes framed in dark lashes. The little girl's hair fell in soft ringlets almost to her shoulders. She was about four years old, Karen judged. She opened the child's mouth to take a look at the tongue. Toward the back of the girl's mouth she detected the diagnostic Koplik's spots.

"I think," she said to the mother, "that your daughter is coming down with the measles. About tonight or, at the latest, tomorrow morning she will probably be covered with a fine rash, and then her fever will go down. In the meantime give her one of these small fever pills every four hours and keep her in a darkened room." Karen explained how the child's eyes could be hurt by bright light and handed the medicine to the mother.

"Call me if she isn't better by morning," she instructed.

"All right. How much, doctor?"

Karen choked back an inclination to say, "Never mind—no pay this time." The mother did look rather poor, but after all Karen had to live!

"That will be one dollar," Karen said. The woman drew a ragged dollar bill from under the belt of her skirt.

"Thank you," said Karen. She had seen her first patient in the mountains and received her first fee. She hoped it did not deprive the family of food!

The next day as Karen was buying a few groceries with the dollar bill, she met the same young mother.

"You are right, doctor!" the woman greeted her. "My little girl is covered with the measles this morning." Karen felt better as she watched the lady order some flour and a few vegetables and pay cash for them. At least the family was still eating!

Karen's practice flourished from the start. The little town was happy to have the services of a doctor, and Karen and her mother made many friends. They often attended the local church on Sundays, since there was no Adventist church.

17

One day the Sunday school superintendent offered Karen a class of junior boys to teach. Karen explained that certain points of her faith were different, but he was not perturbed. "Just stick to the Bible," he said.

Karen accepted the class with its seven or eight boys. Not only did she make it as interesting as she could; she also took the juniors to the woods for afternoon walks and invited them to picnic suppers in her backyard. Soon the boys felt free to call on her with their problems.

There was one boy, Bert, who puzzled her. He was bright enough, but he seemed withdrawn. Karen worried about him and tried repeatedly to make contact with what she felt was the "real Bert."

One afternoon Bert sauntered into the office about closing time. With him was another boy, Tommy, who lived two doors away. The boys chitchatted a bit with Dr. Karen; then they paused as they heard a voice calling.

"Tommy! Oh, Tommy!"

"That's my mother calling," said Tommy. "You wait here, Bert. I'll be right back."

Bert seemed ill at ease. To make conversation, Dr. Karen said, "I suppose Tommy's mother wanted him for supper. It's almost that time."

"Naw," answered the boy, "his mother's always callin' him. I guess she just likes to look at him."

He paused, and then continued: "Reckon he's lucky, at that. I ain't got no maw to call me."

Karen was surprised. "Is that so, Bert? I didn't know!"

"Just a grandmother, and she don't care nothin' about me!"

"Ah!" thought Karen. "So that's what's troubling the boy!"

"Listen, Bert, I was just thinking of having mother make up some sandwiches and a drink for supper and eating in the backyard. How'd you like to join us? Think your grandmother would care?"

"Naw, she won't care."

Bert ate hungrily. In no time at all he had devoured four husky sandwiches and was reaching for his sixth cookie. During the meal Karen learned more about his family. His father had died when Bert was a small lad, and his mother had remarried.

"She didn't want me," he ended sadly, "so she left me with granny. Guess granny didn't want me much either, but what could she do?"

"You can come here anytime you want to, Bert. *We* want you!" she assured him.

From that time on Bert almost lived at Carlson's Cove. He helped Karen clean the office. He mowed and raked the lawn. He emptied the garbage for mother Anderson. In fact, Karen didn't know what she had done before Bert became part of the family. Picnics and outings weren't much fun without him. Sometimes he brought another boy along, but often he was content to be with the two women, whom he called "doc" and "granny doc." Granny doc baked cookies especially for Bert. She made jelly-filled doughnuts and sent them home with him for his school lunch.

Once Karen and her mother paid a visit to Bert's grandmother to see if she had any misgivings about his spending so much time at their home. They found a worn old lady who complained bitterly, "I've raised my young 'uns, and then that Lily come along and dropped another 'un on me. It's 'most more 'n I kin take. Sure, let 'im come to your place. When he's over there he ain't a-pesterin' me!"

Karen's heart ached.

"I wonder, mother," she said one day. "Do you suppose Bert's grandmother would let us adopt him?"

"I don't know," answered her mother. "But what would you do with him if you got a call to India?"

"You're right, mother. Probably we can help him as much just by being friendly."

Toward the end of the summer they missed Bert's visits. He had missed Sunday school also, and Karen was thinking of calling at his home to find out what had happened to him. She knew he could not be sick—at least not very sick—for she was the only doctor within miles, and what other doctor would be called?

One evening at suppertime the front door was pushed open and in rushed Bert's grandmother. "Oh, Dr. Anderson!" she cried. "Come quick! Bert's gone and hurt hisself, and he's lyin' there in the front yard, and he won't talk to me fer nothin'!"

Grabbing her bag, Karen followed the hysterical woman out the door.

"I dunno why he done it," the old lady gasped. "I've allus treated 'im kindly. Oh, hurry, doctor! He was bleeding so!"

In the twilight Karen could see the boy's form lying near the road in front of the house. Tenderly she bent over him, feeling for his pulse. It was weak and thready, almost gone. She lifted the half-closed lids of his eyes; her tiny flashlight revealed dilated pupils. His breath was coming in irregular gasps.

Karen hunted for hemorrhage, and found it over his blood-stained chest. Then she saw the gun where it had fallen near his right hand. Even as she sought to stop the bleeding she realized it was hopeless. Most of the bleeding, she knew, was internal. For a moment she considered calling an ambulance from Boulder. But shortly Bert gave a gasp and was gone!

"Why did he do it?" she asked his grandmother.

"I dunno, doctor," the old lady wept. "I was allus good to 'im."

"Well, there's nothing we can do now," Karen told her. "Let's get you into the house and I'll give you something to help you quiet down. Then I'll call Macketts, the undertakers."

"So he's really gone, doctor!" sobbed the old woman. "I dunno what's been wrong with 'im lately. Last few days he wouldn't eat or nuthin'. Didn't even want to go to Sunday school. He warn't sick, so I just left 'im alone, thinking he'd come out of it in time."

"Yes," thought Dr. Karen bitterly, "you always left him alone. That's the trouble. No love. No one to call his own! Oh, why didn't I ask you to give the boy to me as I was impressed to do?"

She turned and left. As she passed the still form lying in the grass she stooped and softly kissed the warm forehead, letting her

20

tears fall over his face. "I loved you, Bert," she said. "Didn't you know? Would you have done it if you had known?"

For Bert it was too late, but there would be others. She would do more than love them from a distance next time. She would take them into her home as well as into her heart!

Karen was busy in Nederland that winter. She struggled through snow to her knees on many a call to remote mountain places. Once she even rode a railroad "put-put" three or four miles as it snowplowed its way from Tolland to a railroad maintenance camp at East Portal where a seriously ill section hand awaited help.

Ever in the back of her mind was the big question: When would she get that call, the call she lived and longed for, the call she had struggled through medical college for—the call to India?

4- NOT INDIA, BUT CHICAGO

The snow fell all night. The next morning as Karen scraped the frost from the inside of the window she could see the drifts piled high in the backyard. She was glad it was Sabbath, for she was not likely to get any calls unless there was an emergency. By now most people knew about "the doctor's Sabbath."

Karen wondered idly if any of the little group of Sabbath school members who met in her office would be brave enough to venture out. She thought of the first Sabbath she and her mother had spent in Nederland nearly two years before. Life had become quite routine, with only the occasional small events of a country doctor's life to break the monotony. Her thoughts turned, as they so often did, to the mission call of her dreams.

"Karen, would you stir up the fire?" her mother asked. "My, but it's cold this morning!"

"Yes, mother. Reminds me of the day we came here. Remember that snowstorm?"

Her mother smiled. "We have come a long way since then."

"Wonder why I never hear anything from the mission board?" Karen asked.

"Oh, it will come in time, dear. God must have some lessons for you to learn here first."

Breakfast was soon finished, and Karen began arranging the chairs in her office for any who might come to Sabbath school. "Probably they won't come today," she thought. "Too cold and blustery out."

Promptly at 9:30 Karen heard voices outside. Opening the door, she found two ladies and a little girl. Stamping the snow from their boots, the guests stepped inside, and Karen drew them near the stove in the corner.

"You're brave to come out in this weather," she said.

"We wouldn't miss it for anything." Theresa Jones smiled. "Would we, Mary?" Her sister shook her head in agreement as she rubbed her half-frozen fingers together. Theresa removed the woolly cap from her small daughter's head and tousled the girl's curls.

"Even Betty begs to come. She loves the stories you tell and the songs we sing."

Karen smiled contentedly. Life was good in the Colorado mountains, even if it was not exactly the way she had planned to live it.

That afternoon, as she and mother sat reading the Sabbath papers, Karen was surprised to hear a knock on her door. It was the postmaster, Mr. Parks.

"Yes sir, Dr. Karen," he exclaimed, forgetting she was not a "sir." He removed his mittens and unbuttoned his heavy coat to reach the inside pocket. "This is no special delivery letter, but it looks to me like it's an important one. So I said to myself, 'I'm going to deliver that in person to our dear doctor!'" Thrusting the letter into her hand, he added, "It comes from Washington, D.C."

Karen could hardly believe her eyes when she read, "General Conference of Seventh-day Adventists, Takoma Park, Washington, D.C.," but she did not forget her manners. "Thank you, Mr. Parks," she said. "Now let me get you a cup of hot cocoa before you go out into the blizzard again!"

Mr. Parks sat and chatted with mother Anderson while Karen warmed up the cocoa.

"M-mm," the postman enthused. "That sure hit the spot, Miss Karen." As he rose to go, he couldn't resist asking, "Do you think the letter is important, doctor?"

"Yes, I'm sure it's important," she assured him. "And thanks so much for bringing it."

Karen's fingers shook as she tore open the long white envelope. Silence reigned while she scanned its contents; then she smiled and handed it to her mother without a word.

"So your call to India has come at last. Well, dear, I'm very happy for you," said mother.

"But you, mother!" Karen suddenly thought out loud. "What will you do?"

"Don't worry about me. I'll be all right."

"Say, I have it! Why don't you go with me? I believe they would let you if I ask them. You are a nurse and could help me so much out there. Don't you think that's a good idea, mother?"

"I don't know, dear," mother Anderson answered quietly. "I think I would like to go if I could be sure it was the Lord's will. I'll have to think about it, and we should both pray about it."

The news soon spread through the mountains that Nederland was losing Dr. Anderson. People came streaming into her office for a checkup or a farewell chat. Karen did not realize how many patients she had until that last week or two when they all began coming at once.

"Mother, I never knew it would be so hard to leave these folks," she confessed one night.

"I know, dear, but God has called you. We must not look back now."

The General Conference consented to Mrs. Anderson's accompanying her daughter. They were to sail from New York that September. Spring had come in the mountains, and now that there was not so much sickness around, Karen and her mother felt it would be wise to return to Boulder to prepare for the trip to India. It was hard to turn the key in the little cabin door for the last time, but Karen knew she must not look back, for God had called her—at last!

Late one afternoon in August, three weeks before they were to board the train for New York, mother Anderson complained of chills and a severe headache. Karen bundled her off to bed with the admonition, "Now, mother, you stay there! We mustn't let you get sick and ruin our plans."

The next morning a fever had risen, and mother Anderson felt weak and dizzy and could not arise for her customary devotions. Karen lovingly cared for her, using all her medical skill, but by night mother was so much worse that Karen felt she should go to the Sanitarium. There the other doctors confirmed Karen's fears; it was pneumonia. She watched anxiously as the oxygen tent was lowered over her precious mother to assist her with her labored breathing. Karen feared she would lose her mother, but finally, on the fifth day, the crisis passed. The patient's fever declined, and she rested more comfortably.

A week of precious time had slipped by unnoticed. When Karen finally had time to think about personal things, she realized that her mother would not be ready to make the trip to New York and on across the ocean. She wrote a long letter to Elder Kern at the General Conference office, explaining the situation and asking him for a postponement in their sailing date. As she waited for his reply, another important letter arrived.

Several years before, when Karen finished her medical course, she had placed an application with the Chicago Lying-in Hospital for a residency. From time to time the hospital administration had written her that no opening was available. "Would you care to remove the application," they asked, "or should we keep it on file?" Each time Karen had replied, "Keep it on file."

"Someday," she thought, "if I don't get the mission call, perhaps I can learn quite a bit along the line of obstetrics and gynecology. I might even specialize in it."

Now her chance had come. "We have an opening for you," the hospital staff notified her, "beginning the first of January."

Summer had slipped away, anyhow, with mother's convalescence. Now Karen decided she might be of more use to the mission in India if she could have this extra training. Once again letters were exchanged with Elder Kern, and the General Conference committee consented to her request to take a year's residency. Karen felt that this was providential, for mother needed more time to regain her strength. She made arrangements for her mother to live in Dr. Klopfenstein's home while she went to Chicago.

Karen found that Chicago was a mission field in itself. She learned that her first three months were to be spent in the Chicago Maternity Center, from which the residents, interns, and nurses were sent into the homes of the poor to deliver babies. Most of the mothers-to-be were seen regularly at the Center before confinement, so the students were acquainted with their cases. A delivery team was made up of a nurse, an intern, and two medical students, and they traveled the streetcars or elevated railways together to reach the homes. They were admonished to stay together, as it was dangerous to be separated.

"When it is time to make a telephoned report to the Center—and a report must be made at least every two hours—never go alone to do it," their field adviser cautioned. "Take another member of the team, leaving two members with the patient, and if possible take some member of the patient's family along. This is for your own protection!"

Karen was not afraid; she had been reared on the prairies, and had met many a situation there alone. What was there to be afraid of in a city?

She soon found out! One day she was asked to accompany Dr. Langley, one of the instructors, on a postdelivery visit to a patient who was running a fever. As they climbed into Dr. Langley's car he locked his door from the inside and instructed Karen to do the same with hers.

"But doctor," she protested, "it is broad daylight! What could happen to us?"

"Just safer to take precautions," he answered.

The ride through the almost-deserted streets seemed easy enough. It was late in the afternoon, about five o'clock. Although Karen had been present at the delivery a few days before, she was not quite sure of the house. All the houses looked alike, and many of them had no numbers. Finally, after searching through several blocks to no avail, Dr. Langley parked the car in front of a drugstore. "Perhaps I should telephone the Center for better directions," he said.

As he opened the door, two rough-looking men suddenly stood in front of him. One of them poked a gun in his ribs and demanded in a low, threatening voice, "Turn over your car keys!"

"But, the lady!" protested Dr. Langley, with a gesture toward the car.

"Get her out!" ordered the second fellow. "We won't hurt you if you cooperate, but you better hurry!"

"Come on, Dr. Anderson," ordered the instructor. And she was glad enough to get out of the car. The two thugs jumped into the car, turned the key in the ignition, pushed the starter, and were off. Apparently no one had seen the incident; the street seemed deserted still. Where had the men come from?

Doctor Langley turned to Karen. "Well, can you beat that!" was his first remark.

Karen shook her head, feeling as if she had just awakened from a bad dream to find it still bad.

"Have you any money?" Doctor Langley asked her, feeling in his own empty pockets.

"Not a bit!" answered Karen. She had left her purse at home, as the workers had been instructed to do. And this time, riding with Dr. Langley, she had not brought the usual coins for carfare and telephone calls.

"We can't even call the Center," exclaimed Doctor Langley, "unless I can talk this fellow in the drugstore into lending me a nickel!" He motioned for Karen to enter the cluttered drugstore with him.

"Did you see what just happened out there?" he asked.

The clerk shrugged.

Karen felt that the man must have seen the holdup, but didn't want to get mixed up in it.

27

"Will you lend me a nickel so I can call my hospital?" asked the doctor. "I've no money at all!"

The clerk looked at him skeptically. A well-dressed gentleman with a well-dressed lady, and not a nickel between them? After some persuasion on the doctor's part, the clerk grudgingly handed him a nickel, and Dr. Langley called the Center. A car was sent out to bring them home, and the police were notified.

The next day the stolen car was found a few miles outside of Chicago, intact except for two flat tires.

The summer of Karen's residency at Chicago Lying-in was a General Conference year. Elder N. C. Wilson, then president of the Southern Asia Division, came through Chicago to meet the appointee to India. As he rode through the narrow, dingy streets leading to the hospital his eyes took in the degradation and squalor.

"You don't need to go to India, Dr. Anderson!" he told her. "You've got the waterfront of Bombay here under your nose!"

Karen agreed that her experiences in Chicago were good preparation for missionary work. Her heart ached for the underprivileged, and she realized that there still was plenty to do in her own country. Yet India had called, and to that call she responded wholeheartedly.

Karen returned to Colorado eager to complete arrangements for the trip overseas, only to meet further disappointment. Mother Anderson, past seventy, seemed to be in frail health. After correspondence between Dr. Klopfenstein and the General Conference, Karen was told that the mission board did not feel her mother should be sent overseas in such a poor state of health. Since there was no one else to care for the invalid, the call to India was rescinded.

Bitterly disappointed, Karen spent much time pleading with God for her mother's restoration to health. Finally she was able to accept the delay as His will, and she set about to find another place where she could be useful.

5- WHERE HE LEADS

Karen took up her duties again at Boulder and traveled once or twice a week to Nederland to see patients she had known. Finally she decided to return to Nederland full time. She took along a nurse, Lois James; Thelma, a twelve-year-old whom Karen had taken into her home; and her frail but eager mother. The change seemed to do Mrs. Anderson good; her health greatly improved in the crisp mountain air.

"We should have taken Bert into our home, Karen," she told her daughter one day. "He would have been a son to be proud of by now, and we haven't gone to India yet, anyhow."

"Yes, I know, mother," answered Karen, "but at least I learned my lesson; that's why we have Thelma, you know."

"But Thelma is not like Bert. She is so lazy, and it seems all she has on her mind is boys."

"Wrong, mother dear," smiled Karen. "I know she seems to live in a dream world, but sometimes when we are talking I feel that I can help her. I seem to reach through to her, if you know what I mean. At least she is better off here than with her drinking stepfather and her mother away working."

"I suppose," answered Mrs. Anderson. She and Thelma did not get along well together; therefore Karen tried to have Thelma work in the kitchen while her mother was busy elsewhere. Karen had been encouraged about Thelma lately; she had learned to wash dishes clean and to sweep behind the doors and even under the beds! When Karen talked and prayed with her, Thelma

29

seemed to respond. Just in the past few weeks the girl had begun offering halting, childish prayers of her own.

It was while Karen was still interning at Boulder Sanitarium that she had first seen Thelma. Karen had gone with some student nurses to give a Bible study and had been touched by the abject poverty in which she had found a mother and three skinny little girls. Thelma, the oldest, was six years old. Karen longed to take her into her heart and home, but all she could do was to bring her an occasional present. The father, Karen soon learned, spent most of his time and money on drink. The mother often joined him at the bar, leaving the little girls to fend for themselves.

The Bible studies seemed to be helping the mother, encouraging her to seek something more worthwhile for herself and her children. She began to attend church, bringing the little girls with her. The students were able to find some used clothing, which they remodeled into neat Sabbath dresses for the tiny girls. It was rewarding to watch smiles come to the pinched faces. They loved Sabbath school and lived from one week to the next for the moment when their mother would scrub their necks and ears, slip on their pretty dresses, and take them to church. The mother seemed to take pride in making them look as neat and clean as she could. She herself wore an attractive dress, also a gift from the student nurses.

While Karen was in Chicago, she lost track of the family. When she returned, she learned that they had moved to Arizona. One day the postman brought her a letter written in a child's scrawl. "My!" she thought, "I never expected to hear from that child! Let's see; she must be eleven now." Eagerly she read:

> Deer Dokter, Wood you pleze cum and git me? My Daddy left us, and my mama duz not luve us. The nabors are kind, but they don't luv us, You used to luv me. Do you still? If you do, I cud cum to live with you, and I wud sure help you all I cud!
>
> With luv,
> Thelma Higgins

30

Karen looked to see if the address was legible. It was, barely. She sat down and wrote a letter to Mrs. Higgins, expressing her sympathy for the woman's troubles and offering to take Thelma to live with her and be her own daughter. Back came a letter only slightly more legible than Thelma's, "—if you want her, you can cum and git her."

Karen bought two pretty dresses and a doll and made plans to go the next weekend. She bought the dresses small, knowing that Thelma's chances of having reached the size of an average eleven-year-old were slight. She guessed right; the dresses were almost too large for Thelma, but she looked pretty in them, especially when Karen had washed and set the girl's hair.

Karen gave the two little sisters some paper dolls, much to their delight. They started cutting out the pretty dresses at once, and were so preoccupied that they hardly noticed when Thelma waved good-bye from the taxi.

"Good-bye, mamma," said Thelma.

"Good-bye, Thelma. Write to me sometime."

Neither Thelma nor her mother shed tears as they parted.

"How," thought Karen, "can one bear a child and not care any more than that?"

At twelve, Thelma was a smart little girl, and with proper food and rest she began to blossom into an attractive young lady. She attended the eighth grade in Boulder, spent the summer in Nederland with Karen, and the following year returned to Boulder, boarding with friends of Karen's during the week. Weekends she would come home to her foster mother.

"Mother," she said one day, as they drove along the mountain road on one of Karen's calls, "I'd like to be a nurse when I grow up. Then I could help you in the office."

"Yes, dear," smiled Karen, "I would like very much for you to be a nurse. But I have dreams of where you would be helping me in the office, and it's not here!" Then Karen confided in the young girl her dreams of going to India someday.

Thelma's eyes grew round with fright. "But, mother, what if

they should call you before I have a chance to become a nurse?"

A Seventh-day Adventist physician in Grand Junction was about to be drafted into the Army. Hearing of Karen, he sent her a telegram asking her to consider taking over his practice. Karen decided to drive the 300 miles to Grand Junction to investigate. The office was fully equipped and well located, and Karen soon found adequate living quarters for her family. She returned to Nederland after three days to make arrangements to move. It was fall and the first snow was beginning to cover the mountains. Karen was thankful to reach home safely; it had been slippery traveling for the last fifty miles.

Mother and Thelma both approved the move. The packing was soon done. The husband of one of Karen's maternity cases was engaged to move their household furniture and office equipment in his truck, but he was a bit upset because his baby was due and the doctor was leaving. Karen assured him that something would be worked out. She went to bed that night with a prayer that the baby would come before she left the next day.

Sure enough! Shortly before midnight came a knock on her door. "Dr. Anderson, come quickly! Our baby is coming!" urged the excited man.

Before morning Karen presented the trucker with a new daughter. He was delighted and kept saying, "You said you would do it. But how did you know?"

Karen's practice in Grand Junction prospered from the start. She soon found herself with more work than she could do. For the tenth grade, Karen sent Thelma to Campion Academy. There Thelma associated with young people her own age, and soon she was writing Karen that she would like to be baptized. She wrote that she was sorry for the things she had done wrong and wanted mother to forgive her. Karen gladly forgave and thanked God for answering her prayers and leading her girl in the right direction.

Two years later Karen attended Thelma's graduation from Campion Academy and watched proudly as her attractive daughter received her diploma.

In the meantime Karen had developed a personal interest of her own. His name was Elwood Johnson. He was tall and blond, with clean-cut features, and he seemed to be a good Christian. Karen returned his attentions with a bit of reserve, for she could not see how he would fit into her plans for India should their friendship ever develop into something serious. Still, he was pleasant company. It was nice to have someone take her to young people's meetings on Friday nights, and she enjoyed the occasional Sunday-afternoon picnics they shared together. His interest seemed to be growing, so Karen often made him the subject of prayer. Mother liked Elwood very much, actually more than Karen did.

Elder Reese, the local minister, was preparing for a series of evangelistic meetings, and he asked Elwood to assist with the music. Although Elwood had never done this before, he did have a good singing voice, and he agreed to try. Karen noticed his willingness to help, and she wondered whether he might not adapt to mission work somehow.

"Mother," she confided one night, "do you suppose it might have been because of Elwood that God delayed my going to India?"

"I've been thinking about that, Karen," her mother answered. "Yet I cannot see how Elwood would fit into the picture. You know, dear, as I have often told you, God has a plan for our lives. If we submit ourselves to Him each day, the pattern will be woven according to His will. I think we should pray about it, dear."

"Yes, mother. I have been praying about it."

6- RAINBOW TRAILS

The door to Karen's waiting room burst open, and a ruddy-faced young man dressed in a Salvation Army uniform dragged, half carried a moaning woman into the room. Her young husband followed. Karen was standing at her office door.

"Are you Dr. Anderson?" asked the first man.

"Yes."

"Good! I've brought you this case. She's badly burned, as you can see."

Karen worked long and patiently in her emergency room, cutting the clothing from the woman's scorched body, removing the charred debris from her arms and legs.

"Your wife will have to go to the hospital," she told the husband. Then she saw his hands. "Oh, you are hurt, too!" she exclaimed. While she cleaned and bandaged the man's burns, which were mostly on his hands, she attempted to get the story from him.

"How did this happen?" she asked gently, as she worked. The young man, choking back the tears, could not answer at first. The Salvation Army man spoke for him:

"When I found them, Dr. Anderson, their trailer was turned over in the ditch. Their car was on fire. His wife was trapped inside the car, and he was trying desperately to get her out."

"The trailer went out of control," sobbed the husband. "I couldn't hold it. Do you think my wife will soon be all right, doctor?"

"Well, I think she has a good chance, but she will be in the hospital a long time, probably. In several places she has third-degree burns."

"We have had so much trouble lately," the man explained. "You see," he stopped and took a deep breath, trying desperately to control himself, "we were on our way to California. I had been out of work for several months; and my brother, who lives in California, urged us to move out there. He said he could find a job for me, so we finally packed up and left, pulling the house trailer that had been our home for the past two years. Just a few hours after we left home, our baby girl took sick. We stopped to see a doctor in some small town, and he gave us a little medicine for her. But she seemed to grow worse as we traveled. We thought we could reach a town large enough to have a hospital. But before we reached the town the baby went into convulsions and died in my wife's arms!

"That was yesterday. We had an undertaker prepare her, and we bought an inexpensive casket. We planned to bury her near our new home in California. And now this accident!" The man's voice broke as he turned his face to the wall.

Karen's own eyes filled with tears. She gave a sedative to the husband.

The Salvation Army man offered, "I'll ride to the hospital with you in the ambulance, Mr.—?"

"King," supplied the injured man. "Terry King."

At the hospital Karen found that the Salvation Army man seemed to know how to be helpful yet not be in the way. She heard him ask the young man, "Why don't you come home with me for the night? I'm sure my mother would be glad to have you."

Gratefully Mr. King accepted. Karen was thinking, "What a thoughtful young man!"

"Would you mind giving me your name?" she asked him when they were alone.

"My name is Charles Robbins," he answered, flashing her a quick smile.

"You have done a good work today, Mr. Robbins," Karen told him. "How did you happen to find these folks?"

"I was driving over the mountain on my way to a rally. I saw smoke ahead even before I reached the scene of the accident. I always carry a fire extinguisher in my car, and I managed to put out the fire. Then we extricated the woman. Now I should notify the police, and probably they will want Mr. King and me to go back to the scene of the accident with them."

"Yes," said Karen. "Mr. King will be tired, and I am glad you are taking him home with you tonight."

As she turned her car toward home, Karen wondered if she would ever see the personable young man again. The next morning she found that her patient had survived the night and seemed fairly comfortable. Neither Mr. King nor Mr. Robbins was at the hospital that morning.

"Karen," said Elwood one Friday evening a few weeks later, "the young people of some of the other churches have asked ours to join them in a youth rally in this city. Do you think Adventist young people can cooperate in a thing like that?"

"I don't know."

"Well, they want us to come to a 'singspiration' next Sunday night at the Presbyterian church and discuss the possibilities with them."

"No harm in that, I guess," Karen responded.

Sunday evening Karen dressed a bit more carefully than usual. She wore a new blue voile dress and white shoes. Elwood was coming to take her to the meeting, and she was getting rather fond of him. She glanced in the mirror and reached for a little-used bottle of perfume. Then, feeling almost schoolgirlish, she waited in the porch swing.

Finally she saw Elwood's car turn the corner and stop. Disentangling his long legs from the controls, he got out and came smilingly toward her. He was wearing neat gray slacks and a white sport shirt. His coat, she was sure, was waiting in the car; he was a meticulous dresser.

Elwood's tall, lean form towered above her as he offered his hand and asked, "Ready, Karen?"

"Yes," she answered gaily, and jumped up from the swing.

Walking along the flower-bordered path beside her toward the car, Elwood gave a soft, appreciative whistle. "My, but you look pretty tonight!" he said.

On the way to the Presbyterian church Karen told Elwood about the poor family who had lost their baby daughter and then wrecked their trailer and burned their car.

"Seems like some people have all the bad luck," said Elwood. "How is the wife doing? Is she going to make it?"

"Yes, I think so, if no infection sets in. But, Elwood, you know these Salvation Army people? This young fellow who brought them in—he's taken the husband right into his home to live until the wife gets well."

"There's good in them," agreed Elwood. "There's good in all these young people we will meet tonight. I agree that we shouldn't marry out of our faith, but it seems that we could be friendly and cooperative with them."

As Karen and Elwood entered the church, a young man came forward to welcome them. Karen knew she had seen him somewhere, but where? Then it dawned on her! This was Charles Robbins, of the Salvation Army.

"You look different out of uniform," she told him. Then turning to Elwood, she said, "This is Charles Robbins, the young man I was telling you about on the way over here. Elwood Johnson; Charles Robbins." The two young men shook hands.

Behind Charles stood a young man with bandages on his hands. Karen had not noticed him at first; now she greeted him, "Good evening, Mr. King!" She introduced him, also, to Elwood.

As Elwood and Karen settled into their seats he laughed, "Looks like you have a good start at getting acquainted with these 'heathen' young people already." Although Karen knew that he was just teasing, she did not like that remark. How could a boy as thoughtful and helpful as Charles Robbins be termed "heathen"?

Why, she had even found him praying with Mrs. King one day at the hospital, while Mr. King knelt with him.

Karen was surprised to find that Charles Robbins had a prominent part in running the meeting. He welcomed everyone and introduced the minister who was to speak. Later, when the young people were asked to express their opinions as to what they could do to reach the godless youth of the community, he led them in the discussion.

As a result of the meeting, it was decided to hold a youth rally. Committees were chosen, and youth leaders were elected from each church to develop plans for the rally. To her amazement, Karen was chosen secretary-treasurer of the organization. Charles Robbins was program manager. In the days that followed, Karen and Charles often met in committee meetings, and she learned to know him well. She liked the enthusiasm with which he planned his program, and she came to admire the drive which pushed this young man to the front as a leader. "What a wonderful minister Charles would make," she thought.

Elder Reese's plans for an evangelistic effort were nearing completion. Elwood had dropped out because he had accepted employment in another part of the state. He wrote to Karen, and visited her once. But Karen could not feel clearly that the Lord was drawing them together. She often prayed about Elwood and about her lifework. "Does God still want me to go to India?" she wondered.

Mrs. King was at last ready to leave the hospital. Her burns had healed nicely in most areas, although she would need some skin grafting. This could be done after she reached her new home in California, Karen told her. Mr. King could not thank the doctor enough. He was also a staunch friend of Charles's by this time, for he had spent six weeks in Charles's home free of charge.

"I didn't know there were such wonderful people in the world," Mr. King told Charles and Karen. "I hope you will both write to me, because I never want to lose track of you."

With a twinkle in his eye he added, "I'll certainly be writing to you, doctor! At least once a month, with a check enclosed, as soon as I find work."

Karen smiled and wished the couple well as they drove away in their repaired car.

One day Charles brought his mother in for a medical consultation with Karen.

"Mother," he said, "I want you to meet the best doctor in town!"

Mrs. Robbins came often after that, and she and Karen became good friends; so much so that Karen decided to invite her to attend Elder Reese's opening meeting. Quite willingly Mrs. Robbins accepted, and Karen offered to pick her up in her car.

"Thank you, Dr. Anderson, I would appreciate that, for I don't think my son will be home that night." She told Karen how to reach her home.

As Karen drove up to the front of the Robbins home Sunday evening, she was surprised to find Charles, dressed in a good suit, escorting his mother to the car.

"Would you mind if I come along, Dr. Anderson?" he asked.

"Certainly not," was Karen's quick response.

On the way to the meeting Mrs. Robbins told Karen of a brief contact she had had with Seventh-day Adventists on a previous occasion.

"A man came by selling books," she said, "and he was a good salesman! I was so short of cash that I had to rob the boys' piggy bank to raise the down payment. Somehow that man made me want that book. It was *Bible Readings for the Home*, and I often turn to it when something about the Bible perplexes me."

"Yes," agreed Karen, "I know the book well, and it is good."

Elder Reese was an interesting speaker. Karen glanced sideways at her guests occasionally and always found them listening. She felt a warm glow of happiness and prayed silently that these good people might be led to a new experience with Jesus.

Charles and his mother continued to attend the meetings. By the end of the week they had discussed many things with Karen. Charles usually took notes on the sermons, and on Thursday night Karen noticed that he wrote in his notes the question, "Is God particular?" Since this was the subject Elder Reese was speaking on that evening, she was not surprised. But when she saw him add, "Is He particular about the Sabbath?" her heart leaped. Elder Reese had not yet touched on the Sabbath, but Charles was thinking of it! She remembered he had questioned her about it once or twice.

The next night, Friday, as the three of them drove to church, Charles said to her, "Mother and I found that book the salesman sold to her several years ago. Last night I sat up reading it nearly all night." Glancing toward the sun sinking in the west, he added, "Your Sabbath is starting now, isn't it?"

"Yes, it begins at sundown on Friday and lasts until sundown on Sabbath, or Saturday, as most people call it."

"You know," said Charles, "I am convinced that your church is right. I have decided to keep this Sabbath, and every Sabbath from now on, God helping me!"

Karen heard Charles's mother catch her breath. She, herself, was surprised that he should come to so sudden a decision.

"Charles is a man of action," Mrs. Robbins explained. "Once he is convinced something is right he will do it in spite of everything." Karen was not sure whether Mrs. Robbins's voice betrayed pride or irritation.

On Sunday evening Charles told Karen he would not be able to attend the meetings for a while, as he had been sent back to work in the mountains. "I hope you will keep taking mother, though," he said.

"I surely will," Karen assured him.

Karen did not see Charles again until Friday night nearly two weeks later. He was waiting when she came to pick up his mother. As soon as they were in the car Mrs. Robbins informed Karen, "Charles has tomorrow and Sunday off, so he can go to several meetings with us."

Later Charles admitted that he had stretched the truth somewhat. He didn't want his mother to worry, he said, but he did not have Saturday off. He wasn't even sure if his job would be there when he got back! Karen admired him for his courage.

On Saturday evening he further confided, "You know, Dr. Anderson, last Sabbath I had to work—at least, sort of. It wasn't hard work; just directing a bunch of men on the job. But it hurt my conscience. I had kept one Sabbath, and I really felt bad that I wasn't keeping the second one. So I thought I'd take a chance this week. I may lose my job, but I had to keep this Sabbath! I know it is right."

Charles did lose his job. When he came back from the mountains on Monday, jobless, his mother was worried.

"Whatever will we do, Charles?" she asked. "We need your salary to make ends meet."

"Don't worry, mother," Charles comforted her. "I'm sure God will give me another job soon."

But jobs were not so easy to find. The country was recovering from depression, and many men had been out of work. The situation was serious, but Charles never lost faith in God.

Karen tried to comfort Mrs. Robbins. "I'll help you pray that Charles will find another job soon," she told her.

A week after he lost his job Charles came home in a jubilant mood. He chucked his mother good-naturedly under the chin and tossed his five-year-old brother, Buddy, into the air.

"Guess what!" he exclaimed to his mother.

"What, son?"

"God not only gave me one job; He gave me two!"

"Two! How can you hold down two jobs, Charles?"

"You'll see," he laughed. There was a twinkle in his blue eyes. Charles worked the day shift for a lumberyard, and some evenings he was away also. When asked where he had been, he would laugh and say, "On my second job!" He was so mysterious about it all that no one in the family could guess what his second job was. Some evenings, of course, Charles did come home. Those were the evenings Elder Reese's Bible worker came to give Bible studies.

Although Charles's family did not know where he spent his

41

extra evenings, there was someone who did. One evening, after the series of meetings had ended, Karen had found Charles sitting quietly in her waiting room as the last patient departed. He glanced up from a magazine he had been reading and remarked, "Dr. Anderson, I've been thinking—you look so tired at the end of the day. How would you like me to drive for you when you make your house calls in the evenings?"

Karen was pleased, but she hesitated. What would people think? Yet, it would be nice to have someone drive while she relaxed after a hard day's work.

"I think that would be very nice of you," she said, "but can you spare the time?"

"Of course. If I can be of any help to a busy doctor, I can certainly spare the time," Charles assured her.

After that evening it became a regular thing. Charles would be waiting when she finished at the office. They would load her medicine bag into the car and drive off on two or three or even six or seven house calls in the country. Often they would drive fifty miles in one evening.

One winter night as Karen finished her calls and they drove through the darkness toward home, Charles said, "Let's eat at a restaurant tonight."

"Why should we? Dinner will be ready when I reach home."

Charles did not answer, but Karen could see he was disappointed. All evening they had been discussing some points of Bible doctrine between calls. Then he had come up with this idea, and Karen could think of no reason for it, except that perhaps he wanted more time to discuss the subject. The more she thought about it, the more she wished she had agreed to go. As they neared town she said, "Maybe we should stop for something to eat. That would give us more time to discuss this point."

Charles smiled and turned off the main highway toward a sign that said "Childers' Restaurant." All through the meal Karen kept waiting for Charles to resume the subject they had been discussing, but he seemed to have forgotten it. He was in a gay mood. It was nice at Childers'. Karen found herself relaxing and wishing she could come here more often. She thought briefly of Elwood and wondered why he had never brought her here. No letter had come from him for several weeks. Had he forgotten her? For the moment, at least, she did not really care if he had.

The car seemed cold after the coziness of the restaurant. Karen wondered what she would tell her mother. She certainly could not eat again after the meal she had just finished, and if she didn't eat, mother would be worried about her. Before she realized it Charles was turning the car into her driveway.

"Oh, I'm so sorry! I should have dropped you off at home. It's too cold to walk now."

"No, it isn't. I like to walk on brisk winter evenings like this."

He was out of the car in a flash and around to her side, opening the door. As she slid out of the car she glanced upward at the sky. It was dark blue, filled with brilliant points of lights. For a moment she watched in silence. Then she began to point out to Charles the stars she knew.

"There's the Big Dipper—see? And over there's Vega. Do you see the Milky Way?"

Charles was not looking at the sky; he was looking at Karen. Suddenly she asked him, "What was it you wanted to talk to me about at dinner tonight? We were discussing—" What was it they had been discussing? She could not remember.

"Does a fellow have to have a reason for inviting a girl to have dinner with him?" he asked. He was smiling at her as though half amused. Then he whispered, "Good night, Karen," and turned and walked briskly down the driveway.

Karen stood in stunned silence and watched him go. "Good night, Karen," he had said. He had never used her first name before! "Charles must have asked me," she whispered to herself, "because he—because he likes me—as a girl! I never thought of that!" She hurried into the house.

Before she fell asleep she kept hearing the words, "Does a fellow have to have a special reason to ask a girl out to dinner?"

43

7- HIGH noon

When Karen awoke the next morning, the world seemed a golden place. "No wonder," she thought, "that he chuckled when I asked him why he invited me out to dinner! How could I have been so blind? And, it's all too wonderful to be true!"

As she ate breakfast in semisilence, mother asked, "What's the matter, Karen? Aren't you feeling well this morning?"

"Oh, yes, mother! I feel wonderful; I was just thinking about something," she answered brightly. "No use divulging the secret yet," she thought. "Why not enjoy it alone for a while?"

Once in her office, Karen tried to put personal thoughts aside as she busied herself with her patients. About eleven o'clock the nurse called her, "Elder Reese is on the phone, doctor. He wishes to speak with you."

Elder Reese asked if he might come over and talk with her sometime during the day. He did not reveal what he had in mind. "I just want to have a heart-to-heart talk with you, Dr. Anderson," he stated simply.

"All right," answered Karen. "How would four o'clock this afternoon be?"

The minister's opening remarks surprised her. "Dr. Anderson," he said, "I hope you will not take offense at what I am about to say, but I feel that I owe this counsel to you in a fatherly way. You see, a number of church members have noticed you are spending more and more time in the company of Charles Robbins, and we

44

are worried about you. I know it is a personal matter, but he is not a baptized member of our church, although I think he intends to become one."

Elder Reese paused to give Karen a chance to speak. When she remained silent, he continued: "I know these are delicate matters, but I have been concerned about your interest in him—or, rather, your interest in each other. I can't help wondering if, as is so often the case, his interest in the church does not stem from his interest in you!"

After a stunned silence, Karen found her voice. "You may not believe this, Elder Reese, but I never knew that Charles was interested in me as a person until last night!"

It was the minister's turn to be surprised. "But you have been attending young people's meeting with him, and people have seen you together often."

"Yes, I know. But you will notice that on many occasions his mother has been with us, and I always thought that I was doing missionary work by taking them to church."

"Well," said the minister hesitatingly, "that's hard to believe; but I've known you long enough to know you're telling me the truth. But—uh—you said 'until last night.' I don't mean to be personal, but—"

"Yes," answered Karen, trying to be matter-of-fact, "last night was the first time he ever asked me for a date, and you know, Elder Reese, I didn't even know he meant it for a date! I kept thinking he had some point of doctrine to discuss with me. All the time we were eating—he took me out to Childers' Restaurant on the edge of town—I kept waiting for him to bring up the 'problem'! Finally, I even asked him what he had wanted to discuss with me. It wasn't until then—oh, you know—the way he looked at me and all, that I tumbled! Maybe I am stupid, I don't know. But I am telling you the truth! Do you mean the church members have thought we were—going together?"

"Yes, doctor. Even Elwood has discussed it with me."

"Elwood? Has he been in town lately?"

"Twice recently. He says he doesn't think you are interested in him anymore."

"Well, I didn't even know he had been in town! Why didn't he come around?"

"You'll have to ask *him* that, doctor."

"Elder Reese," she said, "I appreciate your taking time to call this to my attention. As you can see, I haven't had much time to think it over. What do you think I should do?"

"Well, doctor, there is one way to find out if Charles is really sincere in his interest in our church, and that is for you to stop seeing him. Tell him you are too busy, or give him some good excuse. I suppose you could tell him there is someone else you are interested in—there is Elwood, you know. Or aren't you interested in him anymore?"

"I don't know, Elder Reese. I only want to do what the Lord wants me to do. I would never presume to choose my own friends. I have always prayed about them, and it seems God works things out for the best when I ask Him to."

"Good girl!" Elder Reese exclaimed. "Now don't you think we should pray about this together?"

"Yes, let's do that," Karen readily assented, and they knelt to seek God's guidance.

At the close of office hours Charles was again waiting for Karen.

"Shall I drive you on calls, Karen?" he asked, flashing his irresistible smile.

"Yes," answered Karen, not daring to look at him. "I will talk to him," she thought, "and try to get him to understand." Before she left her private office, she again knelt to pray that God would show her what to do. She left with a feeling that all would work out according to His will.

As they rode along through the country from call to call Karen felt that something was drawing them together, even as they talked of trivial things. She could not bring herself to end this wonderful thing so soon; she needed time to organize her thoughts and plan what to say so as not to offend him.

"Dinner again tonight?"

"No, thank you," Karen answered softly. "But, Charles, why don't you and your mother come to my home for dinner tomorrow night? There are some things I'd like to talk over with you, and my mother enjoys having your mother visit her so much. Could you come?"

"I think so," answered Charles. "I'll see about mother."

"I'll drop you off at home tonight," Karen said, "and thanks for driving me."

The next evening Charles sat beside her in the living room while their mothers were busy in the kitchen. Karen prayed for strength to carry through the decision she had made.

"Charles," she began, after they had chatted for a few moments, "I think it would be better if we were not seen together. People are beginning to think we are going together."

"Well, I don't mind that. Do you?" he answered.

"Yes, I do mind."

"Oh?"

There was a painful silence, during which Karen almost lost her will to go through with this.

"Well, in that case I suppose there's nothing I can do. I didn't know you disliked me." Charles was the picture of despair. Karen did not trust herself to look at him more than a moment. She hid her face in her hands, crying inside. How could she have grown so fond of this man and not even realized it?

Finally he asked, gently, "Is there someone else, Karen?"

Karen had not planned to bring Elwood into it, but she decided on the spur of the moment that perhaps that might help.

"Yes," she said, "I'm afraid there is. You see, I met him before I did you. And believe me, Charles, I really didn't know you were interested in me—in that way. I only—"

"All right, Karen. I understand. I shouldn't have taken so much for granted. But you see, I never saw anyone around. Is it that fellow you were with the first night of our joint youth meetings?"

"Yes."

"But where is he? He hasn't been to church for a long time."

"He's working several hundred miles from here. He—he writes to me," she added weakly, remembering that it had been over two months since she had received Elwood's last letter.

"Well," Charles said heavily, "if it takes another man to make you happy, then I am all for him." He turned his quick smile on Karen, but she could see the hurt deep in his blue eyes. She turned quickly away to hide her own confusion. How could she feel this way about a man and yet have to sever the relationship so soon? She whispered a prayer that God would help her remain firm.

"You know," said Charles, making an effort to change the subject, "I found in my Bible study last Thursday night some food for thought. Why do you people believe that death is merely a sleep? I prefer to think of my grandmother, for instance, in heaven where she is pleased or displeased with what I do, rather than as a nonentity, waiting for God only knows how many years to begin living again!"

Karen took up the discussion with a heavy heart. She felt as if she had just closed the last door to her own happiness.

Charles no longer waited for Karen when her day's work was over. She tried to throw herself into her work in an endeavor to forget. One night, several weeks later, Charles brought in a patient for the Salvation Army, with whom he still worked at times. As he was leaving he told Karen quietly, "You won't be seeing me anymore for a while. I've taken a job in the mountains again."

Karen's heart sank. Then Elder Reese was right; Charles wouldn't be baptized! She could not restrain herself from asking, "But, Charles, what about your Bible studies?"

"Oh, we've finished those," he answered, "and I've enrolled in the correspondence course. I can study that while I'm up in the mountains." He did not say whether or not he expected to be baptized.

"When do you leave?" she asked him.

"Next Monday. You'll have to put up with my presence in church one more week," he smiled.

"Charles!" Karen wanted to say much more, but why undo all that she had so carefully built up? She sighed and turned away. Charles quickly left the office.

Karen's life settled again into routine. Her chances of going to India, she felt, were growing more remote. Mother's health had improved, but Karen knew the mission board would not send a woman past seventy to a place like India.

Charles was often in her mind, but with sheer willpower she pushed the thought of him away. Often she prayed about it. God must have something in mind for her; she must be patient and trust Him.

One sunny Sabbath morning in June, Karen sat in the church pew quietly scanning the bulletin when she came to an announcement concerning a baptismal service. Idly she wondered who was to be baptized. Suddenly she felt impelled to raise her eyes, and there directly across the isle sat Charles, of all people! He was looking directly at her, and he flashed the familiar smile that characterized him. Could it be? She dared not hope that he would be baptized that afternoon! Yet she did hope.

She was back in the church that afternoon in time to find a good seat. Sure enough, there sat Charles and his mother on the front row with the other candidates! Karen was thrilled as she felt that she had helped to bring these two to Christ. Would Charles someday become a minister as she had dreamed? She breathed a silent prayer for him and added a tiny one for herself. "Oh, God, if it be Thy will!"

Karen greeted Mrs. Robbins with a kiss after the service, and shook Charles's hand enthusiastically, trying not to betray her inner feelings unduly. "We are so happy to have you in our church," she told them, holding Mrs. Robbins's hand with her left one and Charles's with her right.

"And we are so thrilled to be here!" Mrs. Robbins said, her

49

voice breaking with emotion. "Thank you so much, dear, for helping us find the way. You are largely responsible for this, you know."

Sitting alone on her front porch that night, Karen heard his footsteps. Even before she saw him she knew it was Charles. "Oh, thank you, God," she breathed as he came up the steps.

"Good evening, Dr. Anderson," he said quite formally, as he seated himself beside her in the swing. "Do you mind?"

"Not at all!"

"And does the other fellow mind?"

"He's out of the picture," she answered quietly. Then, after a slight hesitation, she questioned, "How was your work in the mountains?"

He told her about it, adding how much he had enjoyed his evenings studying the Bible to complete the correspondence courses.

"Charles, were you planning all along to be baptized?"

"Of course. Why do you ask, Karen?"

"I just wondered." She sighed contentedly.

"I told you, Karen. Remember, on that first Sabbath that I kept, that I saw the Sabbath truth, and I said from that time on I would keep the seventh day? Sometimes in the mountains I met tests but with the exception of that second Sabbath I've kept every one for over three months."

"You would have been baptized even if—" Karen began, then realized she could not finish that sentence.

"You mean, even if I had had no hopes of getting you?" Charles laughed, as Karen turned shyly away. "Karen, when I believe a thing is right I do it. God helping me, I shall always live up to this message, no matter how my friendship with you or anyone else turns out!"

"Oh, I'm so glad!" breathed Karen. They sat on in silence for some time, looking at the stars in the deep blue heavens.

Charles and Karen were married three months later in an afternoon ceremony in the Andersons' living room. Flowers from Mrs.

Anderson's own garden banked the corner where the altar was to be. Elder Reese performed the ceremony, and members of both families were present. Charles's sister Marian was Karen's bridesmaid, and Thelma had come home from the academy for the wedding. Buddy, Charles's small brother, carried the Bible to the minister.

Resplendent in a simple white formal, Karen proudly wore Charles's single orchid on her shoulder and carried a small white Bible tastefully decorated with a few ribbons and rosebuds. The groom could not take his eyes from his bride. Over and over Karen repeated to herself, "God has worked it all out for me!"

After the photographers had taken pictures, guests from the church began to arrive for the reception. Charles had proved his sincerity, and many were the wishes for happiness showered upon the couple. Most of the church friends had heard of Charles's plans to attend Union College to prepare for the ministry. One by one, Karen's dreams were being fulfilled, and Karen was sure there was no happier young lady in the State of Colorado!

Mr. and Mrs. Charles Robbins set up housekeeping temporarily in an apartment on a shady street in Lincoln, Nebraska, in September, as Charles began his studies. But Karen could stay only a few weeks, since they had decided that for the present, at least, she should keep her practice in Colorado.

Neither she nor Charles had realized how difficult the separation would be. Charles came home for Christmas, and in March Karen simply closed her office for a month and went to Union College to be with her husband.

"Never again!" Charles told her. "Either you come down here with me next year or I quit school."

After some deliberation they decided that Karen should sell her practice and move to Lincoln. She found work in a clinic, doing the obstetrical work for a general practitioner. She spent the mornings seeing patients in his office, but her afternoons were free except when she had deliveries. She soon also had a growing practice of her own in the college community.

51

In the spring of 1946, Charles graduated from Union College. Two calls for ministerial internships were open to him. Before choosing one of them he decided to pay a visit to Elder N. C. Wilson, who had returned from Asia and was the president of the Central Union.

"Don't take either one, Charles," advised Elder Wilson, "Not yet, anyway. I think you will be getting a letter from the General Conference in a few days!"

Charles rushed home to tell his wife the good news. Sure enough, within a week the long-awaited mission call had come, and Charles and Karen sat poring over the letter.

"We would like you to go to the Punjab area in northwestern India," the letter said, "to begin medical and evangelistic work among the people there."

India! Karen's eyes filled with tears; her cup was full to over-flowing! Charles was a minister. He was her beloved husband, and they had a call to India!

8- INDIA AT LAST!

Passports, packing, plans! Excitement, adventure! Washington, New York, Cairo, Karachi!

From August to November Charles and Karen waited in Washington for room on a ship. World War II had only recently ended, and reservations were extremely difficult to secure. Charles had spent his time studying in the seminary. Karen finally applied for a license to practice medicine in Maryland so that she could work at Washington Sanitarium while they waited.

Now Charles was leaving for New York for the third time to try to speed things up. Naturally an impetuous young man, it was hard for him to face delay now that they were so near the fulfillment of their dreams.

As Karen watched his train disappear down the track, her heart sang within her. Had not God answered her lifelong prayer? Soon she would sail for India, and God had provided a wonderful companion with whom to share this great adventure! Her heart sang as she hailed a taxi back to the sanitarium.

A few days later the telephone rang. "Dr. Robbins?" an urgent voice inquired.

"Yes."

"Could you get in touch with your husband right away? There has been a cancellation on a BOAC plane for the Middle East, and if you could be in New York by Thursday evening you could go!"

Karen's thoughts raced. This was Tuesday noon. They could try, at least!

Charles's hotel reported that he had just gone out. Karen knew he would probably not be back until evening. Next, she called the Transportation Bureau.

"Yes, we're expecting Elder Robbins in sometime this morning," the voice reported. Karen gave the message and asked to have Charles call her back. Within two hours he called, and he was jubilant!

"I'm sure we can make it, honey," he told her. "You take care of details there in Washington, such as the money and getting our things packed, and come on up as soon as you can."

Two days later in the Piccadilly Hotel, New York, they compared notes. Everything had worked out. Their reservations were ready. The plane was to leave in only six hours.

"Oh, darling, I can't believe it!" Karen exclaimed.

Aboard the BOAC clipper at last, Karen and Charles settled into their seats and fastened the seat belts. Across the aisle were Pastor and Mrs. Mattison, and Miss Emma Binder, all Seventh-day Adventist missionaries whom they had met at the Transportation Bureau an hour before. As the plane rose into the air above New York, Karen glanced out the window at the lights below her. In spite of her elation, she could not restrain a feeling of sadness at leaving her country behind her. Would she ever see it again?

Breakfast the next morning was served in Gander, Newfoundland; lunch they enjoyed "somewhere over the Atlantic," and supper in Shannon, Ireland. For once Charles was satisfied that things were moving fast enough! After touching down in Paris at midnight, in Rome the next morning, and then in Athens, they had a two-day stopover and a change of planes in Cairo. During this brief delay Charles and Karen set out to see as much of Egypt as they could. When they boarded the plane bound for Karachi, they were thrilled to know their journey was almost over.

The plane set down on the Karachi airfield just before sunset on the eve of Thanksgiving. By the time the missionaries had cleared customs and taken the airport bus into town, darkness had settled. Unable to locate the small Adventist mission they knew was in Karachi, they stayed at the Palace Hotel overnight. The next day the two men in the party set out to find the mission.

At that time the mission work in that part of India was in its infancy. Only an apartment and a small chapel marked the beginnings of Adventist mission work in Karachi. Just as the three ladies were ready to sit down to a lonesome Thanksgiving dinner in the hotel, in came the men with Elder P. K. Simpson, who welcomed them warmly and assured them that his wife was preparing a real Thanksgiving dinner for them.

After a week in Karachi, Charles and Karen took the train to Lahore, thirty miles from Chuharkhana, where they were to begin their work. This was it! Now they were on their own, bound for their own mission outpost.

In a moment of weakness, Karen wondered why she had longed to come to India. The people about her on the train were uninviting. Traveling second class, to save the mission money, she felt trapped and suffocated by the strange people about her in their once white, but now dingy, garments. They were mostly men, she noticed. She was thankful for Charles's presence.

During one of the station stops Karen and Charles walked along the platform and saw the women and children crowded together in a special car for women. Most of them were shrouded in their burkas—spooky-looking garments which covered them from head to toe, with only a small open area at eye level.

Even this opening was concealed by crisscross pieces of white material, so that an observer could not detect so much as the color of the wearer's eyes! Thus the Moslem women were protected. How could one ever become acquainted with these ghostlike figures, even if one could speak their language?

Charles was having the time of his life! He had learned a few Urdu words already and went about greeting any man who would listen to him with a gay, "Salaam!" Or he would smile gaily at Karen as he poured boiled water from their thermos, saying,

"Pani [water], dear?" His jubilant spirit was contagious, and Karen found herself anticipating their work. Charles made it fun! How she loved him!

At the railway station in Lahore, Karen was thankful to see that Pastor and Mrs. Morris were there to meet them. Karen soon discovered that they were called "mom and pop Morris." Charles would not have to leave her to hunt up the mission as he had done in Karachi. Soon they were in the Morrises' little car headed for Chuharkhana.

As they turned into the driveway of the academy, Pastor Morris stopped the car and instructed Karen and Charles to walk along the driveway into the school. On each side of the road, spaced several feet apart, were students holding strands of flowers with which they garlanded their new pastor and doctor in the typical Eastern fashion as they sang a song of welcome. Karen could not restrain the tears! These were their boys and girls! No matter that their faces were brown and their clothes different. She knew she would love them just as she had loved other young people in America.

Karen's new home delighted her. There were shade trees and lawns on the campus of the school and around the cement-block house. These were a welcome sight after the deserts through which the train had passed. She set about to make a home of the cottage and to investigate the possibilities for a clinic somewhere on the campus. Charles soon came in with the news that he had heard of an old hospital building in Chichoki, which had been abandoned. Perhaps they could wreck the building and move the bricks to Chuharkhana and build a hospital.

Karen laughed at her lovable, impetuous, wonderful husband.

"Now I know why God sent you here," she told him. "While I try to get things together to start a small clinic, you dream of big things like a hospital!"

"Well," he flashed the familiar smile, "dreams are the stuff that life is made of!"

But Charles did not stop with dreams, Karen soon learned.

56

First the dream, then talks with important people, then blueprints, and finally, as fast as he could push it, the dream come true. Whether it was a hospital, a church, or a school, it was the same. If Karen was too tired at the end of the day to see some patient who came knocking in the night, Charles would see him. Soon he learned enough about common ailments to be able to say, "I think this man has symptoms of a bad cold," or, "This fellow sounds like he's got a stomach ulcer. What shall I give him so he'll be able to sleep? You can see him in the morning." Sometimes Karen would get up and see the patient, but often Charles would save her the trouble.

Charles organized trips into the villages, where he and Karen would vaccinate the people for smallpox or cholera and take care of their minor ailments. With a native girl interpreting for them, where Charles's limited knowledge of Urdu failed, they would see a hundred patients or more in one day and travel on to another village to repeat the procedure the next day.

Most of Charles's time, however, was taken up with evangelistic work. First of all, there was Uplift (or Ingathering) among the businessmen of Lahore, Montgomery, and other cities. Charles, with his friendly, informal ways, soon made lasting friends among the "bara Sahibs" (big masters), and many of them had their first contact with Adventism through his witness during these trips.

On at least one occasion Charles's informality backfired, and he found himself out in the street! Having inquired where a certain English merchant lived, he rang the bell, brushed past the stiffly starched butler who tried to detain him, and entered unannounced into the Englishman's drawing room.

"Good evening, sir," he addressed the astonished gentleman, who was sitting by the fire clothed only in his dressing gown. Slowly the Englishman arose, laid his book aside, and adjusted his pince-nez for a better view of the intruder.

"I've come to spend the night with you, sir," Charles said, turning on his usually contagious smile.

This time there was no responsive smile, and Charles's grin

57

began to fade uncertainly. The Englishman growled, "Not with me, young man! There's a perfectly good hotel in town." Turning to his butler, who stood just inside the door, he directed, "Show this man to the hotel, James!"

Charles backed out with apologies, begging the man's pardon.

In March, four months after their arrival in the Punjab, Charles and Karen were invited to Roorkee for a district meeting, after which they were to be sent to Mussoorie for language school. Charles was particularly happy over this arrangement, as he had been hoping to spend more time studying language.

"You can't get to know these people until you can talk with them in their own language. How can you make the people feel the need of Jesus in their lives unless you can talk to them?" Charles had often remarked to Karen. Now their opportunity had come. Karen also knew that her success as a physician depended largely on her ability to converse with her patients.

Early March in Mussoorie was like being back in Colorado. What a contrast with the heat of the plains! Karen had not known there would be patches of snow in niches along the mountain trails! She loved Mussoorie. On weekends, when she and Charles trudged eight miles across the mountains to Vincent Hill School for Sabbath services, she lived in a world of ecstasy. The majestic Himalayas towering above, the inviting trails which beckoned to them on Sabbath afternoons, the association with missionary teachers at the school, the whistle of exotic birds in the trees—all combined to give Karen renewed strength and courage for the work ahead of her.

9- BIRTH OF A NEW NATION

Contrary to the hopes of the people, the partition of India into two separate nations did not bring peace. Instead, it ushered in a period of violence. In the interchange of people between the lands of Pakistan and India, many acts of cruelty occurred.

Trains going to Pakistan were jammed with Moslems. At the border town of Amritsar just before a train could cross into Pakistan, mobs of Sikhs boarded it and slaughtered every man, woman, and child on it. When the relatives and friends learned of the deed, they determined upon revenge; and the next train going east into India, bearing Hindus and Sikhs, received the same treatment. Thus trainloads of dead flowed both ways across the border, and authorities seemed powerless to stop the massacres.

Terrible floods added to the misery. From the five rivers of the Punjab came the worst floods since the year 1900. Often whole encampments of refugees on their way to "the promised land" were overwhelmed by the rising waters as they slept in improvised tents or on the open ground.

The roads were lined with endless convoys of bullock carts, donkey carts, and many camels carrying salvaged household possessions. Women were walking or riding donkeys; men were carrying little children. In a two-way stream they crossed the border.

It is said that this was the greatest migration in the history of mankind. Over 5,000,000 people were on the move at one time. Such an uprooting of humanity could only bring sorrow and misery. Where were the new homes to house the weary pilgrims?

59

Where were the farms to produce food for the famished travelers? Where were the bankers, the shopkeepers, the factory owners? Most of them had fled to India, being Hindus. In India the situation was reversed, for the places Moslem workers had filled were vacant, and no one had the training to fill them.

In their mountain retreat, Charles and Karen did not at first feel the impact of the great upheaval. The language school had closed its doors, and Charles and Karen moved to Vincent Hill School on the other side of the mountain. Here they felt quite safe. They enjoyed association with the students and teachers, and the battle cries of the Dun valley far below them were but distant rumbles in their ears. But Moslem families living nearby were afraid for their lives. Many of them fled, leaving their homes heavily barred.

One night Karen was awakened by a terrible noise. Shaking her husband awake, she cried, "What was that, Charles?"

Rushing to the door, Charles saw a house on the hill in flames. Within minutes the students had gathered, and, led by some of the teachers, they formed an effective fire brigade. The fire was soon conquered, but the school was no longer in the good graces of the Hindu neighbors, who had set this Moslem home on fire.

Exploring the area early the next morning, Charles and Karen decided to walk up to Valehead, a beautiful home just above their own cottage. Valehead appeared peaceful enough as they approached it, but Charles noted that the front door stood ajar. Remembering the sign he had often read on it as he walked by, "No trespassing. Violaters will be punished!" he cautiously pushed the door wider.

"You wait here," he told Karen, and entered the house. In a matter of minutes he reappeared, his face ashen. "Don't go in there!" he warned. "I've just seen two men who've been blown to bits!" Evidently the owner of the house had set bombs to catch anyone who defied his orders on the front door. Peace could not be long, even for this secluded mountain vale.

Charles and Karen were impatient to return to their mission

station at Chuharkhana where they could be about their work. In spite of the dangers they made plans to return. Early in August Karen wrote a letter to the governor of West Punjab asking for gasoline ration tickets so that they might make the trip home. In spite of poor communications during this war-torn period a letter arrived promptly, containing the desired ration tickets. There was just one hitch: The tickets had to be countersigned by a district commissioner before they could be used. Such was the prejudice against Pakistan that it was doubtful any Indian district commissioner would sign them. As Karen waited she prayed that God would open the way for them to go home.

Karen had a secret, but she did not reveal it to Charles just yet. A few days before they left for home, she paid a visit to an American doctor who was visiting at the school. Her suspicions were confirmed, and that night she announced to her husband, "We are to become parents, my dear, sometime next May! Now, what do you think of that?"

Charles swept his wife into his arms and exclaimed, "Wonderful! We shall be the best parents in all of India—or Pakistan, rather!"

For days he could talk of little else. "Our baby will be the cutest baby in the world. Maybe he will grow up to be a doctor like his mother or a minister like me!"

"How do you know it will be a 'he'?" Karen asked.

"How do I know anything? I just feel it, that's all. But if it's a girl, I'll love her just as much. Don't worry."

Finally, Charles believed he had everything in readiness. He knew the journey would not be easy. Some said it could not be done and advised him to take the train and leave the car in Mussoorie. But Charles felt he needed the car at home, and he was reluctant to leave without it.

The success of the trip was dependent upon getting the ration tickets signed along the way. Two Sikh *munshis* (teachers) who had taught Charles and Karen in language school were anxious to get to Jullundur. They offered to help Charles get the tickets signed if he would take them along. This he agreed to do, and it proved

61

to be a blessing that he did. In several places, if it had not been for the insistence of these men and their acquaintance with the customs of the land, Charles might not have been able to see the district commissioner.

Without serious trouble the travelers arrived at Jullundur, where the two munshis stopped. Then, after replenishing their supply of gasoline, Charles and Karen started toward Amritsar fifty-five miles away. They expected this part of the trip to be the most difficult, and they were right. They encountered roadblocks, bridges out, and obstacles of all kinds. Also the roads were crowded with refugees traveling both ways in all kinds of conveyances or afoot.

As they approached the area of the Beas River, which had been the scene of some of the worst flash floods, Charles and Karen found the going very slow. Sometimes they would be able to travel only a few miles at a time; then they would have to wait for men to dig ditches to drain the roads. Sometimes they had to be rerouted over higher ground. Their station wagon passed truck after truck of Moslems slowly edging their way to the front. From time to time army officers patrolling the roads would stop them and ask to see their passports. When they had left Jullundur behind and traveled the eighteen miles to the Beas River, they met the most stubborn resistance of the trip. It was now Friday morning, and Charles and Karen were hopeful of reaching Chuharkhana by noon. Swinging around the bend of the road, they came suddenly upon a temporary bridge the army had thrown up over flooded land. Guards stood on each side of it, and a voice shouted, "Halt!"

Charles climbed out of the station wagon and held a rather one-sided conversation with the Indian army officer who stood directly in front of the bridge. Unfortunately, the officer understood little English, and although he gathered from Charles's limited Urdu that he wished to cross the bridge and that his home was on the other side, he still shook his head and repeated, "Nay! Nay! No cross bridge. Gov'ment orders!"

In his desperation Charles taunted the guard a bit. "You should join the Red Army. With your determination and loyalty to duty, you'd make a good recruit."

Charles thought the army officer could not understand, but the fellow did get the idea that Charles was making fun of him. Furious, he raised his gun and pointed it at Charles.

"You wouldn't shoot an American, would you?" Charles asked a little anxiously.

"No care. American, Indian, Japanese—no care!"

Fortunately a new arrival diverted the officer's attention. An English army officer arrived in his command car and requested permission to cross the bridge. The Englishman was readily granted passage; but before he went over, Charles begged him for help in ending the impasse. The officer spoke a few words to the guard and motioned for Charles to follow him across the bridge. So, after a two-hour delay, Charles and Karen finally drove across the Beas River.

Although they were now very close to the border of Pakistan, they must still pass through one last Indian town, Amritsar. There they ran into another hurdle in the journey. As they watched for signs in Amritsar directing them onward to Pakistan's first city, Lahore, Charles became confused.

"Karen," he said, "the sign says Lahore is that way." He pointed to the left. "But my sixth sense tells me that's wrong. Don't you think we should go to the right?"

Karen studied the map for a moment. "Yes, Charles. It certainly should be right, but why does the sign point the other way? Maybe there's a diversion, as they call detours out here."

"Yes," agreed Charles, "maybe something is wrong with the road that way." He pulled the car to the side of the road and studied the map with his wife. As a trio of Sikh men with their turbans tightly wound about their heads passed the car, Charles endeavored to ask them the way to Lahore. Shrugging their shoulders they pointed to the sign. Karen noticed a smirk on one man's face.

"Why, Charles," she exclaimed after they were gone, "they know better! They're trying to confuse us." Charles was inclined to agree with her, and kept studying the map. It was Friday afternoon, and Karen was worried.

"Look, Charles." Karen pointed to the west. "The sun's getting low; it's going to be after dark before we reach home if we don't hurry, and we won't be home before Sabbath begins. Why don't we pray about it and ask God to guide us?"

After the prayer Charles looked up to see a distinguished-looking gentleman walking by the car on Karen's side. Leaning over her, he called, "Excuse me, sir. Could you tell us which road to take for Lahore?"

As the man stopped to explain, he kept looking closely at Charles and Karen. Finally he asked, "Don't I know you? Your faces look so familiar. I'm Dr. —— from the Mayo Hospital in Lahore." Instantly Charles and Karen recognized him as a doctor Karen had contacted regarding vaccines the year before. He was most cordial. He told them, "In a few minutes I'll be finished with my business here in Amritsar. Then you could follow me out of the city and on to Lahore. And why don't you stop at my house and have tea with me?"

Karen and Charles thanked him profusely, but declined his invitation, explaining that they had hoped to reach their home before sundown. So he directed them to take the right turn, as they had been impressed to do. He sketched a rough map indicating other turns they must make to get through the city and onto the right road for Lahore.

"That sign," he informed them, pointing to the one which had confused them, "is turned the wrong way on purpose. People living here want to confuse the Moslems trying to find their way across the border. You'll find other similar signs. Don't follow them. Follow this sketch, and you'll be all right."

As they drove on toward home, Charles and Karen both felt God had sent the doctor in answer to their prayers.

Home really looked good to the tired travelers as they turned into the driveway with nearly an hour to spare before sundown.

10- OUT TO THE VILLAGES

"That's right, Shanna, put that box over here—it contains our vaccines, and we can't afford to have them broken. It would be a long time before the government could get more to us."

Pastor Robbins was directing his trusted servant in the packing of the station wagon with supplies for a medical safari. He liked to help Karen bring these drops of prevention to the villages. As if floods and religious riots were not enough for a new nation to bear, the ugly plague of cholera had descended upon Pakistan. Before the people were settled in their new homes, fresh graves had to be dug and loved ones laid to rest. Charles and Karen were determined to do something to help if they could.

"Did you remember the sterile cotton, Charles?" asked Karen.

"Yes, it's in here," Charles answered. Then he added, "This should be fun." Charles loved safaris. He was proud of his wife's medical knowledge and had picked up a lot of it himself by helping her with clinics in the villages. "As long as the English government keeps us supplied with cholera vaccine," he observed, "I think we should make these trips as often as we can. After all, you can't convert a dead man!"

Soon the station wagon was loaded, and, with Shanna to interpret, Charles and Karen set off. They had a good highway for about fifteen miles. Then Charles headed the station wagon onto a sandy road which looked something like a creek bed. Gradually the road grew worse, and Charles was kept busy dodging boulders and mudholes.

Since they had left late in the afternoon, they feared they would not reach Mungoki, the village where they planned to stop. Word had been sent ahead by a native worker to expect them for a clinic. Sure enough, the darkness descended quickly, and they were nowhere near their destination.

"Let's stop the car here on the road and sleep until daybreak," suggested Karen.

"Sure, that would be a good idea," agreed Charles.

But Shanna disagreed. "No," he insisted, "that will never work. As soon as you stop the car, you will be surrounded by people."

"People?" asked Karen. "There are no people around here."

"You will see if you stop, memsahib," Shanna addressed her courteously. "They are everywhere. Out in those fields, in those thickets, in villages close by."

Charles and Karen could not believe him, so they decided to stop. Charles made up a bed for them in the back of the station wagon. Soon Karen heard movements in the brush around them. She heard whispers, too, and raised herself on one elbow to look. In the darkness she could make out shadowy forms moving about. She nudged Charles. What did these men want? Would they do them any harm?

Men were peering into the car. Charles jumped up suddenly, and the men retreated a few steps. Charles shook Shanna awake.

"Ask these fellows what they want," he said. Shanna, rubbing his eyes, emerged from the front seat of the car.

"What do you want?" he called to the shadows lurking in the bushes.

"Tell sahib and memsahib to come to our village to sleep," the men called back. Shanna relayed the message.

"Tell them 'Thank you,' but we will stay here," answered Charles.

But the men did not want to leave. "It is not safe here," they insisted. "Wild animals come, and other men from other villages. Maybe not friendly ones!"

Charles was firm, and after about ten minutes the men slunk

unwillingly back into the bush. Karen and Charles settled down for a good sleep. Shanna was wide awake now and said he would watch. Minutes later they heard voices again. Sitting up, Karen saw Shanna busy in conversation with a group of men not far from the car.

"These men are from another village, memsahib," Shanna said. "They refuse to go away. They want you to come and sleep in their village."

Karen wakened Charles. "What shall we do?" she asked. "These men will keep coming all night."

"Maybe Shanna was right." Charles admitted. "It might be simpler just to go to one of their villages. Perhaps they will let us sleep in our car there and not bother us."

They set out, following the men down the rough road. Upon arriving at the village, they found that the women had prepared a warm drink for them and had laid out charpoys [beds made of rope] complete with mosquito nettings for these honored guests—nothing but the best for the white sahib and memsahib. So out of the station wagon Charles and Karen dragged their sleeping bags.

"This is not so bad," thought Karen as she tucked in the mosquito netting. Things were quieting down, and rest seemed possible at last. But what was this? Suddenly Karen felt the mosquito netting being raised and a cool hand being pushed inside the sleeping bag. Karen froze, but did not move. In the dim light of the moon, she saw that it was a woman. Karen had heard of these things. It was the villagers' way of welcoming a guest, she knew, but it was hard to lie still and be rubbed from head to toe!

Later Karen learned that the trick is to relax immediately and pretend to be asleep so the masseuse will leave. On this first occasion she was unaware of this trick; consequently, she received a lengthy massage. When at last the woman crawled out from under the mosquito netting and replaced it carefully, Karen felt relieved and fell asleep.

The next morning at daybreak everyone in the village, it seemed, was awake. Karen opened sleepy eyes to find native faces scrutinizing her closely. A white woman! What a wonder! White men they had seen occasionally, but never a woman. Everyone wanted to wait on her. Finally, having partaken of hot chapati and boiled milk, Charles and Karen were able to take their leave of the kind village people.

"We must come back to their village someday and hold a clinic, and we must tell them of Christ. They gave us the best they had," said Karen.

When they reached Mungoki, they found that their messenger had done a good job of preparing the way. Karen set her medicines and syringes on the back of the wagon, and Shanna helped prepare the cotton balls in alcohol. As the patients began to gather, Charles recorded their names and helped with the children who were afraid of the shots. In a few hours Karen had given cholera shots to 150 patients. Then they drove to the second village and repeated the operation. They covered seven villages on the three-day trip, and the missionaries felt an intense satisfaction with their work.

At each place, when the medical work was finished, Pastor Robbins would stand up on the back of the wagon and give a short talk, telling the people of Jesus and His love for each one of them. Many of the villagers expressed a desire to accept Jesus Christ. Most of the villages had Adventist workers in them or some layman who could continue with Bible studies after the Robbinses had gone. In their simple way the villagers understood the message of love the missionaries brought them. Village churches resulted from these safaris.

Returning to Chuharkhana once more, Charles was eager to begin work on the building for the hospital. He visited the deputy commissioner of the local district to sell him on the idea of a hospital in his district and asked if the district would consider donating the land and a building just south of the school. This building, he believed, could be remodeled to serve as the nucleus for a hospital.

The commissioner promised to take the matter up with his committee. A few days later he called to say that the building and a lease on the land had been granted to the Adventists.

Charles lost no time in getting at the remodeling of the existing building. He found a crew of boys to help him, and being an energetic worker himself, he inspired the boys to labor hard even when the weather was hot. Soon they had cleaned up the long-unused building, repaired the broken windows and doors, and wired the place for electricity.

Karen watched the work eagerly; but in spite of her hopes, it soon became apparent that the new clinic would not be finished before another important event in the lives of the young missionary couple would take place. There was still much left to be done on that evening late in March when Karen dragged herself wearily home from the old clinic. Her spirits lifted as she noticed that the birds were singing their songs, and the grass was turning green again. She entered the house and sought her husband.

"Charles," she said, "I will soon have to be leaving for Surat." He looked up from the papers on his desk with a start.

"Why, so you will, Karie," he agreed, and his grin broadened. "It will not be long until our little bird will be coming to share our nest. I surely hope he will be healthy!"

Karen smiled, indulgently. "Yes, and I hope she will be a pretty baby and have your curly hair!"

It was a game they had been playing all winter. Charles fully expected a son, and Karen complacently expected a daughter. Not that either of them minded which it might be, but they enjoyed teasing each other about it. The morning that Charles put his wife on the plane for Delhi, India, where she would catch a train for Surat, he quipped gaily, "Tell that little fellow to wait for me—but in case he won't, I'm sending you down early!"

At Surat was a small mission hospital manned by two overseas doctors, an overseas nurse, and a staff of national helpers. Wishing to make sure that nothing could go wrong during the arrival of the baby, Karen had requested permission to go to Surat.

69

Near the end of April, Karen wrote Charles, urging him to come and be with her. She guessed that he would already have his weekend duties planned and would not be able to join her until Monday. But she was wrong. On Friday morning, in he walked chipper as usual and impatient to have the show go on.

It seemed that daddy was just what the baby had been waiting for, because on Sabbath, May 1, 1948, baby Marian Joann Robbins announced her appearance with a lusty yell. And daddy was not the least bit disappointed that she was a girl.

Returning to the school and clinic at Chuharkhana, Karen and Charles were both eager to resume their work. While the equipment needed for the hospital was being accumulated and the building being made ready for occupancy, Charles was sent to Karachi, where he and Karen had landed two years before. Charles was to do some Uplift [Ingathering] work there. As was usual when Charles did this kind of work, he met many interesting people.

One night he sat down and wrote to Karen:

"Today I met the American ambassador to Pakistan, and discovered that he has been suffering with some sort of congestion in his chest. Medicines the embassy doctor has given him haven't helped much. Don't you think a diathermy treatment might help him?

"I told him I was sure it would, so he said, 'Where in the world do you think you'd find such a machine in this country?'

"I told him we had one in Chuharkhana just waiting for our new hospital to be opened. He said, 'How can I get hold of it?'

"So I told him I'd see what I could do. I talked with one of the transportation men in the embassy and also with the doctor, and they both wanted to know if we would be willing to let the machine be flown down here for a few days. That's what I want you to do. Ask Pastor Hamel if it can be done. The embassy would pay all expenses, of course."

Three days later the diathermy machine arrived, and Charles, who had received previous instructions from Karen, gave diathermy treatments to the American ambassador. Within a week the ambassador was much improved, and he and Charles had had many long talks about Adventist medical missionary work.

"What we need," he told Charles, "is one of your hospitals here in Karachi. This is a large city and growing fast. There's not an adequate hospital here. If we could get the city officials interested in building one, do you think you could find the doctors and nurses to run it?"

With typical optimism Charles answered, "Yes, I do."

Nothing more was said about it for a few days; then one day Charles received a phone call. "Come right over, Mr. Robbins," said the ambassador. "There's someone here in my office I'd like to have you meet."

When Charles reached the office, he was introduced to two city officials who were interested in erecting a modern hospital for Karachi. After talking with Charles, they said, "We'll take this up with our city commissioners, Mr. Robbins. We'd be interested in meeting with you again in about a week."

Exactly a week later, one of the men called Charles.

"We are prepared to give you three lakhs of rupees [about $60,000] toward the building of a new hospital if your denomination will put up another lakh. We believe it can be built for that."

Charles was thrilled beyond words. Thanking the men, he told them he would contact church authorities and give them the answer in a short time. He could hardly wait to tell Karen.

Three years later, the eighty-bed Karachi Seventh-day Adventist Hospital was built. The ribbon was cut by the wife of Liaquat Ali Khan, then prime minister in Pakistan's government. Many gifts, such as an iron lung, a fully equipped laboratory, beds, and room furnishings, were given by the well-to-do of Karachi.

All this was the result of the groundwork done by Pastor Robbins, under the blessing of God, during his few weeks in Karachi.

11- THE SHADOW DESCENDS

Tuesday morning, September 7, dawned bright and clear. The cloudiness of the monsoon season with its false promise of rain had cleared, and the heat was again becoming unbearable. Only two small thundershowers had brought temporary relief to thirsty fields.

Dust lay thick along each side of the narrow ribbons of road. In order to pass another vehicle, a car had to slow down almost to a stop, cautiously pull two wheels off into the thick dust, and inch past the bullock cart, truck, or other conveyance. Charles was glad that the station wagon was as large as it was. He found that by playing the game of "chicken" with the stubborn truck drivers he met, and then putting on his brakes and stopping dead in the middle of the road, he could inveigle the truck driver to share the road with him. Otherwise, the trucker, by virtue of being the chauffeur of the larger vehicle, would expect Charles to take all four wheels off the road.

Charles had been to the local bazaar early in the morning. While shopping he heard that three people were coming into the hospital as patients, eager to have the distinction of being the first ones. He bought rice and dhal [lentils] plus a few vegetables and staples. As he wormed his way back along the narrow road, he sang with joy for the miracle of the new hospital made ready in a little more than one year. At nine o'clock there was to be an official opening. The mayor of the town and several other important Pakistani officials would be present. The opening had been publicized in the local paper, and by town criers for the benefit of those who could not read.

For some reason Charles felt very tired, and his head ached. Perhaps he was still tired from his trip to Karachi.

He reviewed in his mind the program for the morning. First there would be music by the young people's choir from the school. Then the assistant pastor would offer prayer. Charles repeated to himself his short speech about the new hospital and what he and Dr. Karen hoped to accomplish. He would thank all the people who had contributed money or time to make the dream a reality and then introduce the speakers from the town. Each of these would say a few words.

Karen was waiting for him when he reached home. "I've just admitted a small boy, dear," she said. "He is our first patient in the hospital. I know we weren't planning to admit any until after the ceremony, but this little fellow needs to stay right here with me so I can work on his diet and watch him. He has TB, I'm afraid. I've put him in a room by himself."

Charles smiled. This was the way it should be. The demand for the hospital and the doctor's services should be such that it could not wait. Somehow, he felt it was an omen of success that a patient should arrive before they were ready. He walked into the hospital and found the nurse busy with the young patient.

"Salaam, Yusifji," he addressed the boy in Urdu. "You are the first one to come."

The boy looked at him with big round eyes, but he did not return the missionary's smile. Charles realized that the boy was frightened; probably he had never been in a hospital before. He lay there staring up at the white sahib with pleading eyes.

"Would you like a story?" Charles asked him.

Solemnly the boy nodded, and Charles began to tell him the story of the Christ child—how He was born on earth, how He grew, how when He was twelve His parents thought He was lost.

A half hour later, as Charles turned to go, the boy asked timidly, "Have you any pictures of—uh—Jesus Boy?"

"Yes, indeed," answered Charles. "I'll see if I can find one." In a few moments he was back with a child's Bible. It was an English Bible, but the lad could understand the pictures at least. He reached for it eagerly.

Later, Charles sat with the town officials, Dr. Karen beside him. The young people's choir had just finished their music. Strange music it was, music of the East with its haunting melodies. The people seemed to enjoy it, and the town officials smiled their approval as the choir sat down cross-legged in the yard. Once or twice during the program Karen glanced at Charles and thought he looked a little pale. She must see that he ate better, she told herself.

When the program was over, the girls from the school served mango squash, a fruit drink, to the thirsty officials and other guests. Tiny cakes of wheat dough, called *samosas*, filled with vegetables and curry and fried in deep fat were also served. Everyone seemed pleased.

Karen started seeing patients in her office as soon as the program was finished. Several times during the busy afternoon she wondered where Charles could be. She was too busy to wonder long; and besides, he had always been able to take care of himself. Still, she had expected him to drop in at the clinic during the afternoon.

When baby Marian woke up from her afternoon nap, Lazar, the trusted servant, put a snowy white dress on her and brought her in to see her mother, who was examining the last patient. The sun was beginning to sink low. It had been a busy day. Marian reached out her arms to her mother, but Karen would not take her until she had washed her own hands thoroughly. "Never know when I might pick up some germ and pass it on to the baby," she told Lazar.

"Where's sahib, Lazar?" asked Karen. "I haven't seen him all afternoon."

Lazar shook his head. "Sahib sick, memsahib," he informed her. "He say his head hurt." Lazar placed his hand over his own head. "He lie on bed all afternoon."

"Why didn't you tell me?" Karen scolded him.

"Sahib say, 'No tell memsahib,'" Lazar explained, as Karen returned the baby to him and hurried to their home. Entering the darkened room, she approached the bed cautiously. If he was asleep, she did not want to disturb him.

"Is that you, Karen?" he asked.

"Yes, dear."

"How did the clinic go?"

"Fine. We saw about thirty patients and admitted four to the hospital. Now we have five inpatients. Pretty good for the first day, isn't it?"

"Yes. Excellent. Thank God for that." He lapsed into silence.

"Are you sick, Charles?" Karen asked tenderly. She knew her husband hated to admit that he felt bad, but she must know.

"Nothing serious, dear," he assured her. "Just this headache. I think it will go away if I rest."

"Poor dear," soothed Karen, stroking his forehead. "You've been working too hard. Why, Charles," she added, somewhat alarmed, "you seem to have a fever!"

Turning to the dresser, she found the family thermometer and thrust it into his mouth. With unusual patience he submitted to her treatment. The thermometer registered 102°.

"You must stay in bed, Charles," she ordered. "You may be coming down with the flu or something. At any rate the rest will do you good. I'll tell Lazar to fix you something nourishing to eat."

"Oh, please—nothing to eat just now. I don't think I could take it."

Karen looked at her husband with growing concern. She questioned him closely but could not make a definite diagnosis. "We'll just have to wait and see what a night of rest will do for you," she decided and left him to sleep while she went to find the baby. So little time she had to spend with their daughter. Marian had even taken her first steps while Lazar was caring for her, and Karen had not seen them. Karen hugged the child close

75

to her that evening and prayed in her heart that nothing serious would be wrong with the baby's daddy.

Karen thought Charles seemed unusually restless that night. He tossed and turned and complained of his arms and legs hurting. Karen rubbed them tenderly and he finally fell asleep. Toward morning, however, he awakened her and whispered in a rather frightened voice, "Karen, it's hard for me to move my right arm. What do you think is wrong with it?"

Karen examined her husband thoroughly. He did seem to have difficulty in moving that arm. Karen thought of subarachnoid hemorrhage, but ruled that out because the onset had been gradual.

She now feared that Charles had something more serious than the flu. As dawn came on, he seemed to sleep more fitfully and would wince with pain when he tried to move his arms. The medication Karen gave him did not seem to help much. About six o'clock he woke up completely and said, "I think I'll try getting into a warm bath if you will heat the water, Karen. Do you think that might help me?"

"It might," said Karen. She went to heat the water. When the bath was ready, she helped him to the tub and noted with alarm that he seemed to drag one foot slightly. She had thought of polio before, but dismissed it from her mind. Now she thought of it again. "Oh, God," she prayed, "please don't let it be that!"

Helping him back to bed, she made him comfortable, then went from the room to read up on the onset of polio. The more she read the more worried she became. When she returned to the bedroom, Charles seemed to be resting better.

"You can go on to your clinic, dear," Charles told her. "I'm feeling lots better." His forehead did not feel so hot, and she was encouraged. Telling Lazar to stay near her husband, she tucked Marian into bed for her nap and went to the new clinic. With difficulty she kept her mind on her work that morning. It seemed that she would never get to the end of the line of twenty-two patients.

"Sahib want something to eat," announced Lazar.

Karen breathed a sigh of relief. "I'm coming, Lazar," she said. "I'll fix it for him."

Charles ate soup and toast with apparent relish. His fever seemed to have subsided, and Karen relaxed beside him for a few moments.

"I think I'll be out of here tomorrow," he told her cheerfully.

"What about your arm?" she asked.

He moved both arms, still with some difficulty in the right one, but with less pain than before.

"I think the hot bath helped," he stated. Karen brought Marian to the door to see her daddy that night. She did, however, keep Marian at a distance, just in case.

As night drew on, Charles's headache returned. He asked for something strong to take it away. Karen knew by this that the pain must be quite severe, for Charles did not give in to his feelings easily. He gulped down the two pills she gave him, using his left hand instead of his right, Karen noticed. "Charles is not left-handed," she thought. "It looks as if he is protecting his right one." She saw it lying limp under the covers.

"Does your right arm still hurt?" she questioned.

"Yes, it does. Do you suppose I could have injured it?"

"I don't know. Do you remember any time when you might have?"

"No."

Karen tried to think. The possibility of polio returned to haunt her, but she pushed it from her mind.

As she prepared for bed that night Charles said, "I hate to suggest this, Karen, because I'd miss you so, but do you think you should sleep in the baby's room on that extra bed? My arm feels more comfortable stretched out like this, and it doesn't leave much room for you."

"All right, if you'd rather," Karen agreed. Before she retired, she gave Charles fomentations to both arms and legs, and finally one to his spine for relaxation.

"That felt good, darling," Charles told her, and managed a smile as she kissed him good night.

Toward morning, Karen was awakened from a sound sleep by a strange noise. She sat up in bed quickly and listened. Yes, Charles was calling her, but what a queer sound! It sounded as though he was struggling to say her name. She jumped out of bed and ran to him.

"Darling," he whispered. "The pain! It is killing me. My chest hurts! Give me something!"

Karen reached for her bag. "What could I give him?" she wondered. "Morphine? Demerol?" In the kitchen, she quickly prepared a shot of Demerol. Eventually he relaxed, but Karen was afraid to leave him, so she wrapped herself in a blanket and slept in the chair until dawn.

That morning Karen called an American doctor in Lahore. "Do you think it could be polio?" she asked.

"Doesn't sound much like it," the other doctor answered. "I suggest you watch him for a while. What you've been doing should help. If you need it, our hospital here is prepared to give more serious help."

Karen hated to ask the dreaded question, but she knew she must. "Do you have an iron lung?"

"Yes," answered the doctor, "but I hardly think you'll need that. The onset has been too slow. If this is polio, it is certainly an atypical case and should not be a very serious one."

Karen felt reassured. She was happy to find Charles breathing evenly when she returned to the house. She gave instructions to Lazar to call her immediately when sahib awoke, and went to the hospital to see her patients. It was still an hour before clinic time, but the courtyard was already full of waiting people. She summoned her nurse. "I think we will begin the clinic now," she said. "I may need to get away early this morning."

"How is Pastor Robbins?" asked the nurse, concerned.

"Not much better," answered Karen. "Remember him in your prayers."

"We surely will; and we have, Dr. Karen, ever since he's been sick."

The day passed without much change in Charles's condition. Night came on, and Karen dreaded it. Like most patients, Charles seemed to get worse at night. Karen prayed that this night he might take a turn for the better.

Tucking baby Marian into bed, Karen realized that it had been three days since Charles had been able to cuddle his daughter. What wonderful times they had enjoyed together, he and his precious girl! Karen remembered one of the last nights Charles had taken a few minutes to play with Marian. He had gotten down on all fours and pretended to be a bear. Marian had squealed with delight as he had come toward her growling. Backing up to her mother, she had hidden behind her skirts until daddy grabbed her and threw her into the air. Marian loved it all.

"Now you'll have to cuddle her awhile," Karen had told him. "Otherwise, she will be too excited to go to sleep."

So Charles had settled into the rocking chair with a storybook, until Marian was sleepy. "Will I ever see a scene like that again?" Karen wondered.

That night Karen had Lazar move a cot into Charles's room for her. It was well that she did, for a little after midnight Charles awoke, choking. "My chest!" he gasped. "I can't—breathe!"

Karen threw back his covers. "Oh, darling," she sobbed. She grasped his arms and began to move them in unison up over his chest and out again over the bed, rhythmically.

"Better?" she asked.

"It—helps."

Suddenly she made a decision. Running swiftly to the servants' quarters at the rear of the house, she awakened Lazar.

"Run, quick!" she told him. "Get Mr. Alexander. Sahib is so sick. We must take him to Lahore right away."

Back she rushed into the bedroom. Charles was gasping for breath. She began again to administer artificial respiration.

"My legs!" he murmured, "they're—gone!"

"Oh, God, please save him!" Karen cried out in her distress. "Oh, why doesn't Brother Alexander hurry?" She bent tenderly over her husband, pushing down on the count of ten and pulling up to rest for another count of ten. Somehow she managed to get her clothes on as the men were lifting Charles into the station wagon bed, and she shouted to Lazar to take care of Marian. Then she clambered into the station wagon beside her husband and continued the artificial respiration.

"Take him to the Mayo Hospital in Lahore," she told the driver. "They have an iron lung there. He's got to have it."

"Oh, God," she prayed, still counting to herself by tens, "please let the iron lung be empty, and please help us to get there!"

Three hours later Charles was safe in the iron lung, and it was working satisfactorily. The doctor she had called the day before told her, "Good work, Dr. Robbins. You saved his life on the way here."

Karen could not believe that Charles was really in that horrible iron lung, that her worst fears had materialized, that he really had polio or something equally serious. Yet the doctor confirmed her suspicions. "We can't be sure until the tests are run," he told her, "but it surely looks like polio now. I never heard of such an unusual onset, though."

After an hour's sleep, a bath, and a bite of breakfast, Karen rushed back to the hospital. But what could she do? Charles seemed to be resting comfortably as long as the machine did its work. She talked with him a little, but he seemed quite sleepy. "Probably some sedative the doctor has given him," she thought.

Mostly, she spent her time praying. Surely God wouldn't bring them all the way to the mission field and then let Charles die. Surely God needed him still! She thought of baby Marian at home and wondered if Lazar had fed her a good breakfast. She was thankful for Lazar. He loved that baby as much as he did his own. He would take good care of her. Bless him!

Charles stirred. She bent low to catch his words.

"Don't worry," he was saying. "I'll be all right, dear. In a few more days I'll be out of this thing and home with you and Marian."

"I'm sure you will, darling. I'm not worrying. We must trust God to heal you, and I know He will."

Days dragged by, and still Charles could not leave the iron lung. Word came from the General Conference to buy a new iron lung which Dr. Karen had written them about. It was one she had previously seen in Lahore. This was installed in the Johnsons' home where Dr. Karen and Mr. Deweltz, who had been one of Pastor Robbins's first converts, took turns caring for the sick man. The Johnsons were the Adventist missionaries in Lahore.

As he lay there helpless, Charles often asked Karen, "Why do you think God allowed this to happen? Do you think I will ever be well again? Am I to die in this thing?"

When thoughts of discouragement swept over him, Karen did her best to dispel them. But the time came when she must tell him the doctors' verdict.

"Charles," she said one morning late in November, "the doctors think it will be a long time before you will be able to get out of this lung. The General Conference has offered to fly us home; we might be able to get a little better care in the United States. What do you think?"

Charles's eyes clouded with tears. "You mean, leave our beloved country? Why, we have just begun the work here!"

"I know, dear, but perhaps we could return later—when you are well." Karen knew it was a faint hope, but she must cherish it anyhow.

There was a long silence. Then Charles said quietly, "Yes. When I am well."

12- NIGHT

"Karen," said Charles one morning in early December, as she sat beside his iron prison, "I wish you would get the Bible and read a little to me this morning."

"Is there anything special you would like me to read?" she asked.

"Yes. Please read the thirty-seventh psalm."

When Karen had finished reading the entire psalm, Charles said, "Now read the fourth verse again."

"Delight thyself also in the Lord; and He shall give thee the desires of thine heart."

"That's it—the last part," exclaimed Charles. "Isn't that a wonderful promise? Do you know what the desires of my heart are?"

"I have an idea."

"Yes, I think you do, my good wife. You know that above all things the desire of my heart is to see you and my mother and father in heaven. Would you do something else for me, dear?"

"Of course, Charles."

"Get a pen and paper. I want to dictate a letter to my mother. No! On second thought, I won't have you do it; she might think it was your idea. Please ask Mr. Deweltz to come here and take it down."

He dictated the following letter to his mother:

"Dear mother,

"This is a beautiful fall day in Pakistan. As you know, our

winters are like fall at home, and the birds are still singing in the trees beside me here on the porch where they have moved me. God is very near to me this morning, and if it is His will that my life should end this way, I am willing and ready to go. But before I go, I wish you would let me talk to you as we used to talk together before I was married.

"I was about the age my little brother Buddy is now when I got my first job. Remember, mother? Times were hard, and dad's job didn't pay much; I was proud of my ability to help out. Marian was still in school, and I should have been, but I felt more needed in the breadwinning line. Later, after Karen and I were married, I did get to finish my education; so it was all right. In fact, I can see God's hand in it, for the Christian education I received later has been worth much more to me.

"Remember, mother, when I met Karen? And later I took you to her office so you could meet her? Somehow, I knew even then that she would be my wife someday. I know now that it was God's way of bringing us to a knowledge of salvation. We had not really known God before we attended those meetings in the little Adventist church—not in the way we found Him there. A new sense of His great sacrifice for us swept over us; we studied our Bibles closely. Is God particular, we asked ourselves?. . .

"Well, you know the story—we were convinced by the Holy Spirit, and we could not resist His pleading any longer. A new peace swept over us such as we had not known before, and we decided to take up our cross and follow Jesus. Not that we would be able to keep the moral law in our own strength, but that by God's help we could observe all those Christian principles we had always aimed for, anyway, with the exception of the fourth commandment. . . . When we failed in any of these points, we knew that the grace of Jesus Christ would cover our sins, and we would be saved in spite of our sins, if only we believed on Jesus. Oh, mother mine, how precious that newfound truth was to us! How precious it still is to me!

"I do want to meet you and daddy and the rest of my family in heaven, my own dear mother! Having once known and understood these things, God will hold you and me responsible for them. If He had not shown us, if He had not led us into new truth, then we would not be judged by it. But now that we have known it, there is no turning back. . . .

"My little brother Buddy—how much it would mean to him to be able to give his life to Christ unconditionally now, as he enters upon young manhood.

"I want you to forgive me for anything I've ever done or said to you which hurt you in any way or which was not right. I have tried to prepare myself for dying, if that be my lot. God will take care of Karen and my precious baby whom you have never seen, and I know He will take care of you, too.

"So good-bye, mother, and always remember, I love you and hope to meet you in heaven. God bless you!

"Your loving son,
"Charles."

As Charles finished dictating the letter, Karen came to the porch and heard the last few sentences. Choking back the tears, she looked for something cheerful to detract Charles's attention.

"Look, Charles," she said, "there is the lovely bulbul bird of India. He is singing his heart out to you. That is to tell you that you shall have the desires of your heart. Someday your father and mother will meet you in heaven, but God may have other plans for you now. Do not be impatient, and never give up hope, for maybe it is His will to heal you yet."

"Yes, Karen, if He sees best. If not, I hope He will let me rest soon, for I am so tired and such a care to you this way. And what good am I to anyone, really?"

"You must not talk that way, dear," Karen warned him quickly. "Your very patience is inspiring to many who come to see you, and God has granted you time to make all things right between yourself and your fellowmen and between yourself and God. You yourself have pointed that out." Karen dropped a light kiss on his forehead and went into the house.

There were letters waiting for her—one from her mother, and a note from the Simpsons in Karachi saying that they would be glad to help her get Charles transferred from the train to the plane in Karachi and headed toward the United States. Another letter, one she had been waiting for, was from the General Conference: "Arrangements are now complete. . . . The portable equipment has been sent by plane to Karachi. . . . Two doctors have been assigned to meet you at the San Francisco Airport. . . ."

Karen's eyes filled with tears of thankfulness. Yet, would Charles make it? Could he? What if he should die up there in the air somewhere over the Pacific? It seemed an awful risk to take, but what else could she do? If Charles could get to the White Memorial Hospital in Los Angeles, she felt sure the doctors there could give him treatments that would be helpful, even if they could not entirely restore him. Briefly she prayed. Then she went out to tell her husband about the letter.

Charles received the news eagerly. Anything was better than lying there with no improvement day after day. At home there would be nurses and doctors to take over the constant vigil his wife was giving him. Their baby needed her, too. Little Marian was growing up without a mother. Two long months he had lain there, hoping, praying, dreaming.

On Thursday, a week before Charles, Karen, and tiny Marian, with Mr. Deweltz to help care for Charles, were to leave for Karachi, Karen noticed that Charles's face seemed unusually flushed.

"Too much excitement, this getting ready to move," she thought as she stood watching him while he slept. "Oh, God," she prayed, "if it be Thy will, grant him the strength to make this trip. If not—" She stood with folded hands and aching heart, repeating the words that sprang from her personal Gethsemane, "Thy will be done!"

By Friday morning Charles's chest had filled with fluid until he was hardly able to breathe. "Pneumonia," thought Karen. Deep down she felt that the trip was not to be.

She spent every available moment with her beloved husband.

All through that night, his chest kept filling, and he was unable to raise the obstructing fluid. With a small hand syringe Karen patiently removed it. This gave him temporary relief, but she had to repeat the operation every few minutes. His temperature rose. Toward morning she saw his lips moving and bent low to catch his words.

"Darling," he gasped, "I feel—that we—will never make—this trip. It is not—God's will. I think—He is going to take me—from you—soon. Don't grieve—I am ready."

Karen could not answer. She squeezed his hand and sat quietly by, feeling his pulse grow weaker and weaker, hearing his breathing grow more sporadic.

Why must she be called upon to go through this? What would she have to live for when Charles was gone? Yet she would not keep him if it was best that he go. She could not ask that he suffer more. Fighting back the tears so that Charles might not see her grief, she performed the needed tasks and waited.

Early Sabbath morning Karen saw that Charles was choking up again. Reaching for the suction, she turned toward him. But on his face was a look of joy. The choking had subsided. He turned toward her with a smile, closed his eyes, and was gone!

Karen did not leave at once. His still-warm hand lay in hers, and through her tears she whispered to his unhearing ears, "Good-bye, darling. But not for long. In a few short years Jesus will surely come to reunite us."

Pastor Justin, a national worker whom Charles had loved, preached the funeral sermon. Karen knew this was the way Charles would want it. Out in the little grove of neem trees, where they had often walked hand in hand on a Sabbath afternoon, the grave had been dug. Karen watched the casket as it was slowly lowered into the ground.

Turning to take Marian from the trusted servant's arms, Karen hugged her baby close as she thought, "There is life here—his life, his child! God is good. 'The Lord gave and the Lord hath taken away; blessed be the name of the Lord.'"

THE BREAK OF DAWN

The crying of her child awakened Karen the next morning to a world without Charles. She threw back the covers and went to clasp the baby to her breast. Oh, how thankful she was for baby Marian!

"What shall I get you for breakfast, darling?" she asked, in as cheerful a mood as she could summon.

To her surprise, the baby lisped, "Coco, mamma."

Only once before had she put two words together. At the sound of her child's voice, Karen laughed out loud, giving her little daughter a hug. "You funny baby!" she exclaimed. "If you want a drink of water you say 'coco.' If you want milk, it's 'coco.' I guess anything liquid is 'coco' to you!" Suddenly the room seemed warm and cozy and filled with love.

She could hear Lazar building the fire out on the porch to heat water for washing. She knew the loss of his beloved burra sahib had been hard for Lazar. Charles had reciprocated the servant's love, treating Lazar more as a friend than as a servant. The bond between them had been close, and Karen knew her servant's heart, like her own, must be heavy. His slow, deliberate actions told her so. Forcing herself to assume a cheerful air, she outlined the day's work with Lazar.

"We must carry on, Lazar," she said. "Sahib would want us to. When we are sad and lonely like this, we will feel better if we can force ourselves to do the necessary tasks about the house. Work is a blessing."

"Yes, memsahib," he answered respectfully, but still looked gloomy.

Baby Marian stretched out her arms from her high chair.

Lazar lifted her from the chair and cuddled her in his arms, running his lips through her soft brown hair. Karen was glad the child liked her servant so well. What would she have done during those long weeks of Charles's illness without Lazar? Oh, God was good. He could foresee everything and make provision for it.

Karen and Marian spent Christmas in Lahore with Pastor and Mrs. Johnson and their three children. Karen tried to make it a happy occasion for the little girl's sake, for each time Marian would catch her crying the child would pat her mother's face and say, "Daddy." Karen prayed daily that God would help her be cheerful for Marian's sake.

A few days after Christmas, when they had returned home, Karen went to the garden to gather vegetables. Lazar must have something to prepare for dinner: fresh carrots for creaming, sun-ripened tomatoes for salad, peas which she and Charles had planted together. "Charles!" she thought. "Life does go on, even though half of one's heart has died."

After she had carried the vegetables into the house, she tiptoed to the door of Marian's room. The child was playing contentedly with her teddy bear. Slipping quietly away, Karen headed out into the sunshine again.

Questions raced through her mind as she walked along. Where was she going from here? Should she go home, or should she stay where she knew the need was so great? Ahead of her she saw lonely days and lonely nights. How could she stay?

On and on she walked, unconsciously drawn toward the neem grove where lay the new grave. Silently she stood above it as her tears fell.

"What shall I do with my life now, Charles, my beloved husband?" she asked in her heart.

As clearly as though he had spoken to her came the words

she had often heard him say, "With God's help we must carry on, though the way seem closed and the road impassable."

"We must carry on," she repeated to herself. "Yes, that is what he would want me to do—carry on. I must not run back to the States where it would be so much easier to rear my little girl, not close down the clinic and the hospital he worked so hard to build, not turn my back on all he has struggled for. I must carry on."

Turning back, she walked through the arbor which led to the hospital compound. Entering the halls that Charles had so recently completed, Karen walked with a new elasticity in her step. Finding a piece of cardboard on her desk, she pulled a pen from the drawer. She made a sign in Urdu and tacked it to the clinic door:

CLINIC HOURS BEGIN TOMORROW, JANUARY 2,

at 9 a.m.

Karen Robbins, M.D.